Printed and Published in Great Britain by D. C. Thomson & Co., Ltd.,
185 Fleet Street, London, EC4A 2HS.
© D. C. THOMSON & CO., LTD., 1990.
ISBN 0-85116-499-4

(Certain stories do not appear exactly, as originally published.)

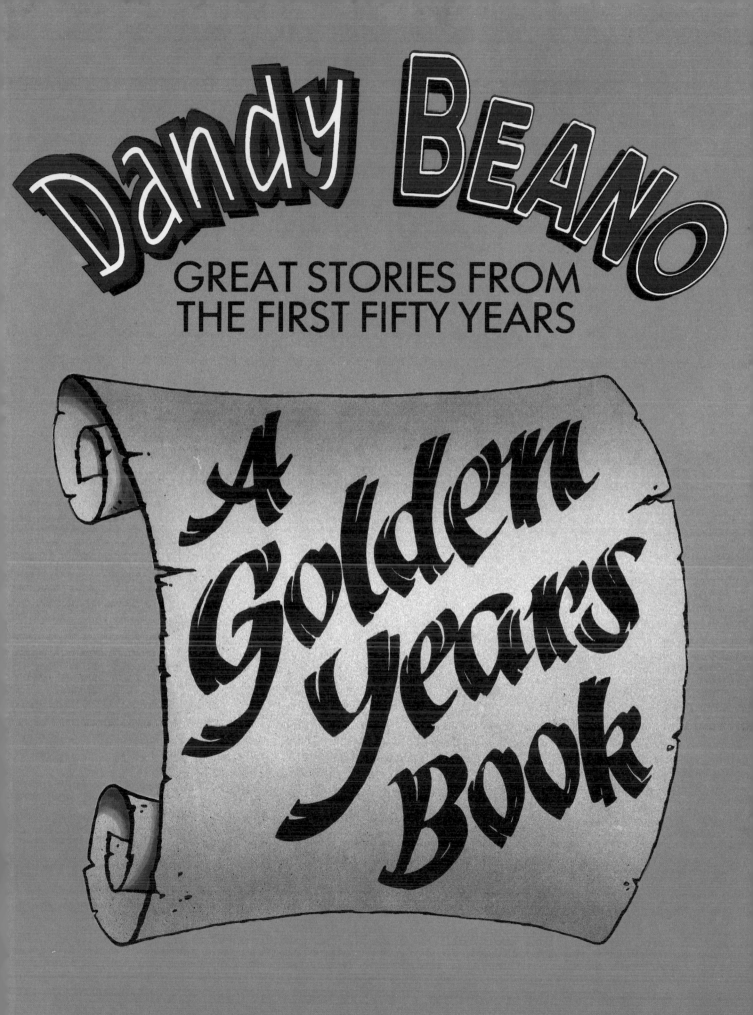

NCIENT iron hinges groan, a stout wooden door creaks slowly open and out they rush . . . heroes every one! Legendary figures from the pages of Dandy and Beano.

Red Rory with his mighty eagles, tiny Tom Thumb and lanky Danny Longlegs, General Jumbo, Britain's youngest commanding officer, high-flying Jack Flash and axe-wielding Crackaway Jack . . . the list goes on. Famous names that thrilled millions of young fans.

The great adventure stories began with Dandy and Beano's earliest issues in the late 1930's, when the two comics were the latest titles from the publishers of such well-established boys' favourites as Wizard, Rover, Hotspur and Adventure. Those publications were packed cover to cover with exciting serials that undoubtedly inspired many of Dandy and Beano's early adventure stories.

The golden years for the two comics' heroes were the 1940s and 50s, but Black Bob, General Jumbo and a few other 'survivors' were still entertaining young readers decades later.

Now, for the first time, the heroes from both Dandy and Beano can be found between one set of covers . . . exciting stories, thrilling stories, great stories from the first fifty years.

A GOOD LONG READ...

Laughter has always been a crucial ingredient in **Dandy** and **Beano's** success , so it should come as no surprise that many classic adventure stories mixed giggles and guffaws with the thrills and spills. Two of the best examples of this style were the exciting exploits of tiny **Tom Thumb** and the tall tales of **Danny Longlegs.**

The **Tom Thumb** story overleaf appeared in **Beano** in July 1947, and the **Danny Longlegs** saga that follows is from the **Dandy Book** of 1951.

TOM THUMB
THE BRAVE LITTLE ONE

1 — Tom Thumb and Tinkel, hiding in a crow's nest high in a tree-top, peered down on Jorgo the Giant. Only an hour before the tiny heroes had escaped from the giant's clutches, and now they watched the monster man as he strode along with a great club over his shoulder. The giant was angry, and the little men wondered where he was going in such a rage.

2 — So interested were the little comrades in watching Jorgo that they were not aware that a crow had alighted on a twig behind them. The bird's beady eyes glittered with rage when it saw the tiny figures in its nest. Suddenly, with a harsh croak of rage, it fluttered forward. One thrust of its beak sent Tom spinning out of the nest, and an instant later Tink was dropped over after him.

3 — Just at that moment, Jorgo was passing under the tree. The giant had a huge hunting horn slung over his shoulder. Poor Tom and Tink hurtled downwards — and fell straight into the mouth of the horn. Jorgo had captured them without knowing anything about it. The little chaps were jammed tight in the neck of the horn. They could not move!

4 — Jorgo the Giant strode along until he came to the face of a towering cliff. There he stopped and unslung his hunting horn. "My slaves will be pleased to see me," he chuckled. Inside the horn, Tom and Tink shivered as they heard the giant's booming laughter. Then Jorgo put the horn to his lips, and tried to blow a blast on it. But no sound came from the horn!

5 — The giant was annoyed. "What ails the Wonder Horn?" he muttered, shaking it hard. Then he drew in a great breath of air, put the horn on to his lips once more, and blew with all his might. Jorgo's lungs were powerful. The pressure shot Tom and Tink out of the horn like bullets from a gun, and sent them sailing into space. Luckily for them, Jorgo did not see them whizzing through the air.

6 — Tom and Tink were blown clean into the branches of a tree. As they clung there, the tiny heroes saw an amazing sight. The blast that Jorgo had blown on the Wonder Horn had caused a great stone door, set in the cliff-face, to swing inwards. Now Jorgo was striding into the big cave that lay behind this strange door. And from beyond the door came the sound of children sobbing and moaning.

7 — From the depths of the big cave, Jorgo led forth a line of little captives. The children blinked as they came out into the daylight. Up in the tree, Tom and Tink stared at the strange scene. "See! The children are in chains!" whispered Tom. "Where is the cruel monster of a giant taking them? We must try to help them. Come, Tink!"

8 — Jorgo blew another blast on the horn, and the door of the cave closed silently. Then, holding the end of one chain to which four boys were held by iron waist bands, Jorgo stalked off. By then Tom and Tink had reached the ground. When Jorgo's back was turned, they seized their chance, and, leaping up from the grass, caught hold of the chain between the two boy slaves.

9 — The young slaves saw the tiny figures clamber up on to the chain. Tom Thumb raised a finger to his lips in warning. The lads understood and kept quiet as Tom clambered along the links of the chain towards the leading boy. Jorgo strode through a gloomy forest without looking once behind him. Had he done so, he would have seen Tom and Tink whispering into the ears of the leading slave. When at last Jorgo halted, Tom had worked out a plan which might succeed in freeing the young slaves, who were being forced by Jorgo to build a castle for him.

10 — The work on the castle at the edge of the forest had not gone very far. Jorgo, having made fast the chains of the young slaves to stakes driven into the ground, lay down on the ground and soon fell asleep. This was the moment Tom and Tink were waiting for. The young slaves had told them that Jorgo always fell asleep while they worked. When this happened, a stray dog that lived in the forest would come out among them. They had made a pet of this dog ever since Jorgo had carried them off from their village to be his slaves.

11 — When the little dog appeared, Tom and Tink soon made friends with it. Then they tied a piece of cord round its neck. The other end of the cord they tied to the Wonder Horn, which lay on the ground beside the sleeping Jorgo. Then they climbed on the dog's back and rode off, pulling the horn behind them. Ten minutes later Jorgo awoke and saw that the horn was gone.

12 — Jorgo was mad with rage. He could not believe that he had lost the horn. "Maybe I dropped it as I walked o'er the forest path," he growled. "I will search for it!" So Jorgo gathered his slaves, and went back the way he had come, looking everywhere for the horn. But Tom and Tink had reached the cave by the time Jorgo and his slaves came in sight!

Adventures

1 — Jorgo the Giant had lost the Wonder Horn, whose note was the only key to the door of his secret cave. The giant had discovered his loss while his boy slaves were working on the walls of the castle which he was forcing them to build. At once, Jorgo had set off to look for the horn, for he thought he might have dropped it on the way through the forest. Behind him, in chains, he dragged the slaves. Now, Jorgo had arrived back at the cave and found the huge stone door open. Tom Thumb and Tinkel had stolen the horn, and managed to blow it hard enough to open the door. Jorgo peered inside the cave.

2 — Behind the giant's back, the young slaves were ready to put into action the plan which Tom Thumb had worked out. Some of the boys had picked up a long wooden pole which lay near the mouth of the cave. Jorgo was still looking into the dark cavern, when, using the pole like a battering ram, the slaves charged forward. The end of the pole struck Jorgo in the back, and, for all his great size and weight, the giant was sent sprawling into the cave. Tom Thumb, perched on the shoulder of one boy, gave a cry of joy! "Blow the horn!" he cried. "Make haste! Give Jorgo no time to escape from the cave!"

3 — Tom and Tink had hidden the Wonder Horn in the grass, but they had told the slaves where it was. The huge horn was soon hoisted to the lips of Hal, the Bowman's son, and an instant later the deep note of the horn rang out. Jorgo's roars of rage were cut off as the great door, obeying the horn, swung shut.

4 — Inside the cave, Jorgo scrambled to his feet. The huge man was bursting with rage, for he had heard Tom Thumb's shrill cry and now knew who was to blame for trapping him in the cave. Jorgo glared at the inside of the stone door. Then he raised his heavy club and swung it with all his giant strength.

5 — The cries of joy from the boy slaves died away as they heard the sound of Jorgo's club pounding on the cave door. Tom Thumb tugged Hal's ear. "Into the cornfield, quick!" he shouted. "See! The door is cracking!" Tom spoke the truth. Under Jorgo's mighty blows, the great door was being shattered. The slaves, who had just had enough time to break off their chains, ran to hide in the corn.

6 — But the runaways were too late to get into hiding. As they raced through the tall stalks of grain, Jorgo burst out of the cave and saw them. "Run!" he bellowed. "But, never fear — Jorgo will come a-reaping!" The giant turned back into the cave, and a moment later he reappeared. On his shoulders perched two hooded falcons, and he was carrying a scythe!

7 — Mumbling and muttering, Jorgo strode to the edge of the cornfield. The young slaves, hidden in the cornstalks, trembled as they heard the scythe blade whistle through the air. As the keen edge lopped off the stalks, Jorgo began to shout out threats. "I'll boil you all in oil!" he roared. "All of you will die. And the two little midgets I will feed to my falcons!" Tom and Tink, who were creeping along as fast as they could, heard the scythe shear through the corn only a few inches behind them.

8 — To avoid being cut in two by the next stroke of the scythe, little Tom and Tink had to leap upwards so that the blade passed under their feet. At the same moment, Jorgo noticed Hal crouching on the ground, and pounced on the cowering boy. Then the giant's quick eye saw another movement in the stubble as Tom and Tink raced towards a mouse-hole. Jorgo stooped and grabbed at the tiny comrades, but he was too late to stop them. The little pair vanished into the hole.

9 — Startled field-mice scurried in all directions as Tom and Tink came running down the narrow tunnel. Tom had drawn his sword to beat off the mice, if necessary, but the mice were afraid of the tiny humans. Up above, Jorgo was stamping on the ground in an effort to crush the mouse burrow. Luckily for Tom and Tink, and the mice, Jorgo was stamping in the wrong place. The earth trembled, but the burrow did not collapse.

10 — By following the tunnel, Tom and Tink crawled into the open again at the edge of the field. Peering over the top of a little ridge, Tom saw Jorgo rounding up the slaves. All at once Tom gave a cry of alarm. "Beware, Tink!" he yelled. "Two falcons have sighted us! Run!" The tiny fellows ran for their lives, but they had no chance of escape. Because of their bright clothing, the falcons could see them easily.

11 — Tom and Tink swerved and dodged. More than once they avoided the sharp claws by the breadth of a hair. But in the sand Tom tripped over a small stone. Tink saw the accident, and bravely ran to Tom's side. As the little black boy tried to help Tom to his feet, both falcons swooped down. The chase was finished. Tom and Tink were caught, and the falcons flew back to Jorgo, each carrying a struggling figure in its beak.

12 — Jorgo had rounded up all his slaves and tied them together. When his falcons brought back Tom and Tink the giant was full of glee. "Oho, my brave falcons! Ye shall feed well for this!" he chuckled. "Ye shall eat the little mites who dared to meddle with Jorgo the Giant!" Then Jorgo scowled at Tom and Tink. "Your cunning will not help you now, mannikins! Jorgo has proved too clever for you!" he snarled. "Now you must die!"

1 — Tom Thumb and Tinkel, his tiny comrade, were in the tightest spot of their lives. The midget heroes were held fast between an enormous thumb and forefinger. And glaring at them from close range was the evil face of Jorgo the Giant, who held them prisoner! Brave though he was, Tom Thumb could hardly stop his tiny knees from knocking. Jorgo the Giant was forcing a gang of boy slaves to build a castle, and Tom and Tinkel had roused Jorgo's anger by attempting to free the young slaves. The giant had vowed to kill the mites for this.

2 — But, though Tom and Tink were in dire peril, help was not far off. For hidden among the uncut corn in the harvest field where Jorgo sat were some of the young slaves whom Tom had tried to aid. One of the slaves had overheard Jorgo's grim threat and his nimble brain was busy. From his pouch he drew flint and tinder, and lost no time in kindling a small faggot. Jorgo, seated on a pile of wheat sheaves, was too busy gloating over the tiny pair of adventurers he held prisoner to notice what was happening behind him!

3 — Stepping silently nearer to the heap of cut wheat-straw, the boy slave thrust the faggot into the pile. The fresh summer breeze was enough to fan the fire. The wheat-straw crackled and burst into flames. A second later Jorgo's howl of pain split the air as the flames stung his skin, and he dropped Tom and Tink.

4 — When Tom Thumb landed in the stubble he rolled over, and was on his feet in a trice. Followed closely by Tinkel, he left the leaping, bellowing Jorgo and headed at top speed for a hollow tree-trunk which lay at the edge of the field. They were not quite quick enough. A howl behind them told that Jorgo had seen them!

5 — The giant had beaten out the flames which had charred his clothing, and now he came lumbering across the field. Running along inside the hollow log, Tom gasped as the daylight suddenly blacked out. Glancing back he saw the furious Jorgo's head and shoulders thrust into the open end of the tree trunk. At that moment, Tinkel pointed upwards. "Up here, Tom," he cried.

6 — Following Tink's pointing hand Tom's eyes lit up. A large hole in the hollow trunk offered a way of escape, and in a flash the agile pair had scrambled up into the fresh air. From there it was a simple jump to the branches of a bush which overhung the log. Suddenly, Tom drew his tiny sword. "Wait, Tink!" he cried, and pointing to a wasps' nest hanging over the hole in the trunk.

7 — From the tree trunk below came the rumbling growls of Jorgo as he crept into the hollow log. Tom Thumb leaned out and slashed at the wasps' nest with his sharp sword. An angry buzzing began as the nest dropped through the hole in the trunk. Jorgo, stung in a dozen places, tried to scramble out of the hollow trunk, but stuck fast. With an effort, he scrambled to his feet.

8 — Mad with the pain of a hundred stings, Jorgo staggered around, encased in the hollow trunk. The cloud of wasps that hovered around his face prevented him seeing some of his young slaves creep up on him. Two of them held a length of rope between them. Next moment Jorgo tripped over the stretched rope, and toppled, like a falling tree, to the ground.

9 — With a tremendous crash, the tree trunk hit the ground. Then there was silence. Tom and Tink, despite their tiny legs, were first to reach Jorgo's head. The giant's eyes were closed — and as the boy slaves gathered round, Tom shouted, "Jorgo has been knocked senseless — now's our chance to settle with him! This is what we must do."

10 — Swiftly, Hal the Bowman's son bent an ear to listen to Tom's plan. A smile spread across the boy slave's face, and, straigtening up, he explained the plan to his comrades. Loud cheers greeted his words, and without more ado the youngsters bent willing shoulders to the hollow trunk. In a minute they had it rolling towards the nearby river!

11 — Tom and Tink urged the boys on. A final mighty heave sent the tree trunk, with Jorgo inside, splashing into the river. The sudden shock brought the giant back to his senses, and he began to bellow threats, but, wedged tight in his wooden prison, he could do nothing. Half an hour later, seated astride the floating trunk, seven of Jorgo's ex-slaves were paddling on their way to their home village, where the evil giant would be handed over to the authorities for punishment. And, paddling alongside, in one of Jorgo's shoes, were Tom and Tink! Behind, using other floating logs, came the rest of the freed slaves. It was a long time since Tom had seen his father and mother, and weary of adventuring for the time being, he had decided to go home, too. He was taking Tinkel with him to visit his parents, and to tell them the stories of his thrilling adventures. So, for the time being, Tom and Tink were saying goodbye to their journeyings. But both of them knew that some day they would set out again in search of new adventures.

DANNY LONGLEGS

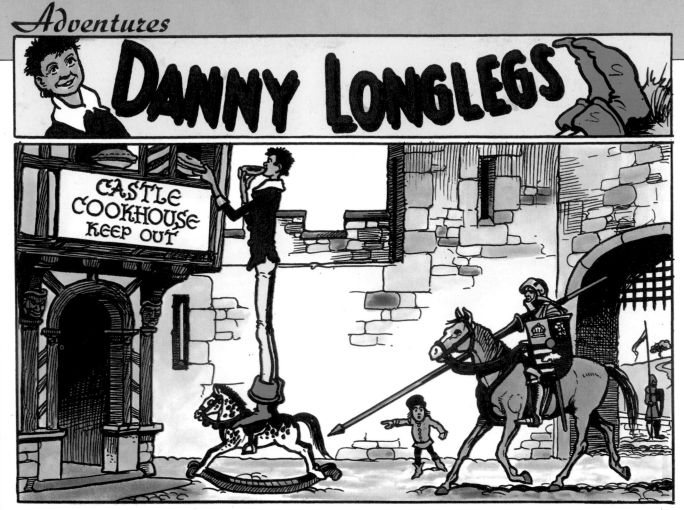

DANNY LONG was mighty hungry, which wasn't surprising, for a schoolboy who is ten feet tall and still growing needs a lot of grub to fill him up. Longlegs was his nickname in the old-world village of Sleepy Valley where he lived, and he was using his long, long legs and arms to reach some tarts in the kitchen of Castle Bower. Unfortunately the kitchen window was too high even for him, and he had to stand up on a toy rocking-horse to reach it.

2 — This was unfortunate, because Sir Standfast Bower, who owned the castle, espied his tarts being pinched. And he rode quietly forward to topple Danny from his perch by yanking the rocking-horse away from beneath him. He used his long lance to do the yanking, and Longlegs came down to earth in a hurry. This made Danny's prank doubly unfortunate, because in his crash the rocking-horse went smash — and it belonged to Sir Stan's young son!

3 — The castle servants and men-at-arms came crowding round in answer to the shouts of the knight, and they grabbed the tart pincher. Sir Standfast heard his young son complaining about the broken rocking-horse, and he had a great idea. "Put the tall one on rockers," he ordered. "My son will not be robbed of his fun as his mother was robbed of her tarts!" The men-at-arms sprang to action, and soon Danny Longlegs was transformed into an outsize rocking-horse.

4 — "Think you're funny?" muttered Longlegs, trying to speak with a bit in his mouth. "But I'll get my own back. Just you wait!" Sir Standfast didn't wait, because he was going off on a boar-hunt, and he wanted to quaff a quart of foaming ale at the village inn before the hunt began. Off he went, leaving his children to make the most of their outsize rocking-horse. And they did — rocking on Danny's long back till poor Danny was as tired as an old nag!

5 — It was a whole hour before orders were at last given by Lady Bower to release the culprit. Longlegs limped into the village with cramp in his long legs and thoughts of vengeance in his mind. When he got there the sight of a circus which advertised a talking horse gave him an idea. Here was a chance of the very revenge he wanted! He had a long talk with the owner of the talking horse, which, of course, wasn't a horse at all. The circus man was willing to help.

6 — Danny borrowed the horse-skin and got inside it. It was a pretty good fit for him, for the talking horse normally had two men inside it, and what fitted two men was just right for one ten-foot boy! In his disguise, Danny ambled along to the door of the village inn where he proceeded to get rid of Sir Standfast's horse. He also took the knight's two pages into the plot, and they agreed to keep mum. Danny stood waiting on all "four" legs on the spot where the real horse had been.

7 — "And now I'm off to bore myself on a hunt for a boar," said the laughing Sir Stan when he came out of the inn and climbed into the saddle. He was too pleased with his own wit, and too full of ale, to notice that though he climbed into his own saddle it wasn't on his own horse! And nobody thought it wise to tell him! "Gadzooks, old Stormalong grows more bony every day," muttered Sir Standfast, patting his horse's neck, which was really Danny's knobbly shoulder.

8 — Danny said neigh like a horse, and with a false nicker and an imitation whinny he pranced off into the forest. He now had Sir Standfast right in the hollow of his hand — or rather, back! But while he was thinking of how to make his revenge complete, a strange thing happened, a thing that had never happened before on Sir Stan's boar-hunts — a boar came charging at them! Sir Standfast was still, his eyes blinking in dismay. But he didn't sit still very long!

9 — Longlegs was so taken aback that he rose up on his hindlegs just like a horse. But he stayed up on them, which wasn't like a horse. Sir Stan crashed on his back with a clatter of mail, and rose groggily just in time to climb a tree before the boar gored him. The tusker at once turned from the man to the horse. It didn't seem to like horses, even imitation ones, so it chased Danny round and round the tree. It wasn't a merry-go-round for Longlegs.

10 — "I'm getting dizzy," gasped Danny, and he pulled away the false horse-head to see where he was going. "Make room for me up there!" he called to the surprised knight, and Sir Stan was pretty well stunned to hear a boy's voice come from this strange horse which ran around on its hindlegs. Longlegs leapt to clutch the tree-branch with his forelegs, and Sir Stan shook himself and shouted, "Why, you're not my horse!" But he had no time to say any more.

11 — He just got the word "horse" out when the branch broke off under his weight. So his voice broke off — and then the grunting of the boar broke off, for Sir Stan in his heavy armour fell right on top of the charging tusker. And that changed its name from boar to pork, for the brute was killed stone dead when the knight fell on it. It was the first boar Bower had ever killed, and he was very pleased. So he said nothing at all about Danny's trick.

12 — Sir Standfast invited Longlegs home to Castle Bower for dinner. And what a dinner that was! Roast pork, grilled bacon and stewed sausages, all made from the dead tusker. They formed a feast that filled Danny up properly for the first time in years. In addition, Sir Stan's son and his pals got a new horse made of the boar's head and hide. "It's maybe not a rocking-horse," said Sir Stan, "but what's wrong with having a rocking-pig?" And so said Danny, too.

YOUR BEANO FLIGHT GUIDE
(FLIGHTS OF FANCY — NO TICKET REQUIRED)

DECADES before today's youngsters were enjoying package holidays with their parents, **Beano's Jimmy Watson** was a seasoned traveller, thanks to the magic patch on the seat of his pants. But it wasn't fun in the sun for Jimmy! One wish and the magic patch transported him back through time to witness the great events and meet the famous names of history. The story overleaf first thrilled readers of the 1951 Beano Book.

JIMMY *and his* MAGIC PATCH

OOMPAH — oompah-ta-ra-ra-boomtah! The Southtown Silver Band came marching down the High Street on a Saturday afternoon, and bang in the middle of the band, thumping away merrily at the big drum, was our pal, Jimmy Watson. Jimmy was just learning to play the big drum — and every time he missed a beat the bandsmen got all mixed up and out of step.

2 — Poor Jimmy! He thought he was a hero helping out the band because the real drummer was ill, but he could hear some of his pals laughing at him as he marched into Queen's Park for the afternoon concert. "I'll show 'em," he muttered. "I'll be a famous drummer boy yet." And just then Jimmy caught sight of an old statue of Napoleon which stood in the park.

3 — "I wish I was Napoleon's drummer boy!" muttered Jimmy. Now Jimmy had a Magic Patch on the seat of his pants. The Patch had been sewn on by an old gipsy woman, and it had the power to whisk Jimmy back through time. No sooner had Jimmy made his wish than — whoosh! — he was on his way back through the years to join Napoleon's army as a drummer boy.

4 — Gosh! Jimmy's heart was in his snow-covered boots as he picked himself from a snowdrift and found himself in Russia. He had joined Napoleon and the French Army in the famous retreat from Moscow in the year 1812. But you can't keep Jimmy Watson down for long. "Cheer up, Sir," he said to Napoleon. "It's only two thousand miles from here to Paris."

5 — Jimmy kept banging away at the drum to keep himself warm, but nobody was listening. Most of the troops had their ears wrapped up to keep out the cold — and they couldn't hear Jimmy's music anyway! Still, Jimmy thought he was doing fine as Napoleon's drummer boy until he tripped over his own feet and went head-over-heels into the snow. That decided him.

6 — "I'll be a drummer boy to somebody who'll appreciate me," muttered Jimmy. "Maybe the Duke of Marlborough would like to have me on his side. I'll make a wish and see." And no sooner had Jimmy wished than he was whizzing through the air, back through a hundred years or so to join the Duke of Marlborough, who was fighting a war for England, on the Continent.

7 — Trust Jimmy to join the English army at the wrong time! The Magic Patch landed him back in the year 1704 — slap in the middle of a battlefield, with the English troops on one side, and the French troops on the other. A charge was just about to begin and Jimmy was glad he had brought along his drum. For the first time that day he was going to find it useful.

8 — Jimmy dived like a rabbit underneath the drum. "Oh, Mother!" he gulped. "Someone's going to get hurt here!" The battle was going strong now. Cannon roared. Bullets whined. Steel clanged against steel. No wonder Jimmy longed to be back in the Southtown Silver Band. He shut his eyes as the soldiers charged with fixed bayonets.

9 — The two armies closed on one another, and Jimmy was right in the middle of no man's land. Drum or no drum — if he didn't shift himself smartly, he was certain to be used as a doormat by soldiers of both sides. "Oh, gosh!" gasped Jimmy. "I wish I was back in Queen's Park." Whoosh! The Magic Patch whisked him like magic from the battlefield.

10 — Pretty soon Jimmy found out that the Magic Patch was playing a trick on him. Instead of taking him back home, the Patch was landing him at the entrance to a big park where a stately Queen was preparing to step down from a magnificent coach. It was Queen Elizabeth — and she gaped as Jimmy's big drum landed in a puddle which lay right at her feet.

11 — And in two shakes Jimmy landed beside the drum just in time to give Queen Elizabeth a helping hand over the puddle. "Allow me, Your Majesty," he said, and the Queen stepped down on the drum and reached dry ground safely. The Queen was delighted. "You're as polite as Sir Walter Raleigh. You must join us in our picnic," she said.

12 — At the mention of picnic, Jimmy's mouth watered. The Queen's courtiers had brought along a huge hamper packed with the finest eats Jimmy had ever seen. The big drum served as a table, and Jimmy found something even harder to beat — the poshest picnic he'd had in his life. He had a swell time before the Magic Patch whisked him back home again.

Adventures ALL ABOARD!

During the hey-day of **Dandy** and **Beano's** adventure stories, you had a better chance of spotting The Loch Ness Monster or shaking hands with a Yeti than meeting one of the comics' heroes on the number nine bus. **Tom Thumb, Danny Longlegs,** and the rest of the gang knew much more exciting ways of getting around.

▼ Joust a minute! That's not a real horse it's . . . The Horse That Jack Built.

▲ An ice little sledge for Young Strong-arm, The Axe-man!

▲ The crew of **Shipwrecked Circus** have the perfect excuse for being late . . . their train was held up!

◀ **Tom Thumb** is flying today . . . and frying tonight if he can land that fish in his pan!

▲ **Danny Longlegs** likes to travel by jumbo, and we don't mean jumbo jet!

When **Turtle Boy** says ▶ he can travel farther on shell, he's not talking about petrol.

GINGER'S SUPER JEEP

Ginger's Super Jeep may not have looked as impressive as his fellow heroes' forms of transport, but readers of the 1957 Dandy Book discovered there was more to Ginger's cart than met the eye.

YOUNG Ginger Griffiths whistled cheerfully as he sped along a country road on the outskirts of Greentown. He was tootling along at a steady thirty miles per hour, but he wasn't in a car or on a motor-bike. He was sitting in a soap-box cart!

The cart was really Ginger's Super Jeep and it looked pretty much like an ordinary soap-box cart except that it was fitted with green wheels. A space-man from Venus had given Ginger the green wheels and they were super-special. They could do some extraordinary things like making the Jeep go fast for instance.

"Soon be at Midtown Bank at this rate," murmured Ginger. "This is the easiest half-crown I ever earned."

Mr Matthews, the manager of Midtown Bank, who lived in Ginger's road, had gone to work that morning without his reading glasses, and Mrs Matthews had given Ginger a half-crown when he offered to deliver the specs.

Ginger's whistling stopped abruptly when he heard a rushing noise above his head.

"Suffering cats!" he gulped.

Over the road, not many feet above Ginger, glided a small, single-engined aeroplane, its engine spluttering. It skimmed through the tops of some trees and then vanished from view.

"He's in trouble," snapped Ginger, sending the Jeep diving towards a gap in the hedge.

The strange green wheels could take the cart over any kind of ground, and in another moment Ginger's Super Jeep rolled zig-zagging in and out of the trees towards where the diving aeroplane had disappeared.

The trees soon ended, and Ginger found himself in a small meadow surrounded on all sides by tall trees. And there, instead of the aeroplane being wrecked, it was standing all in one piece at the far end of the field.

When Ginger reached the aircraft, the pilot was climbing down from the cockpit.

"I expected to find you badly hurt," said Ginger. "That must have been a really tricky landing you made."

The pilot nodded.

"Didn't think I'd manage," he said, mopping his brow.

The pilot, who said his name was Ted Johnson, explained that his engine had suddenly cut out on him, and he hadn't had time to choose a better spot for landing.

"But getting out of here is another question," he went on, looking around the meadow. "I'll have to get some engineers to dismantle the plane and take it away by road."

Ginger thought for a bit, then he snapped his fingers excitedly.

"I've got an idea," he said. "I can't cut down those trees without the owner's permission, but I'm sure he won't mind me giving them a haircut! While I'm pruning them down a bit, you fix your engine trouble, and then this is what we'll do . . ."

As Ginger unfolded his plan

Ted first looked doubtful, and then thoughtful, and then he gave Ginger a pat on the back.

"It might work, youngster," he said. "If that little jalopy of yours will do all you say, I'm game to have a go!"

So while Ted stripped off his flying togs and went to work on the aircraft engine, Ginger drove towards the trees at one end of the field. On the way he unclipped from the side of his Jeep a strange gun-like gadget whose barrel was surrounded by scores of small cylinders. These cylinders were bung full of gases, each of which had a different effect. Ginger spun the cylinders until one marked DISSOLVING GAS was in line with the barrel. Then he drove his Jeep straight for the biggest tree.

But instead of the Jeep running smack-bang into the tree, it reared up on its back wheels and drove straight up the trunk! Those green wheels could cling to a vertical surface like any fly!

Straight up the tree went Ginger and the Jeep, and then Ginger, the "barber", stopped twenty feet up to give the trees their "haircut"

He levelled his Gasgun at the base of the nearest tall branch and pressed the trigger. At once a thin jet of dark brown gas streamed from the barrel, and as it touched, the wood dissolved into dust and the branch fell to the ground.

Ginger played the jet over the tree, until a third of the tree-top had been removed. That was enough to let the plane pass over and yet not kill the tree.

Then Ginger turned his attention to another tree, and then another and another. Finally he backed down his own tree and gave it the dissolving treatment, too.

When he reached the ground he surveyed his handiwork proudly. A broad stretch of the trees at one end of the field had all been trimmed down by a good ten feet.

"Ted's plane should be able to clear that now," said Ginger, and he turned to drive back.

But something stopped him dead. Ted Johnson was standing with his back to the aircraft, with his hands raised in the air. And pointing a pistol straight at the young pilot was a sinister-looking man.

Ginger didn't understand what was going on, but he could see that Ted was in trouble.

Ginger couldn't risk a jet of gas for fear of harming Ted. He bit his lip thoughtfully, and then spun the cylinders of the Gasgun until one marked BURNING GAS was in line with the barrel.

"Hope Ted uses his wits and knows what to do when I fire," he muttered as he carefully aimed the Gasgun to strike some yards behind the swarthy man.

Ginger pressed the trigger and a jet of dense green smoke shot silently through the air. As it hit the ground at the spot where Ginger had aimed, it burst into a roaring crackle of flame.

by some foreign government and he's been after me for some time. He usually has another man with him — an Englishman who looks like an ex-convict."

"But why are they after you?" asked Ginger inquisitively.

"They want the papers containing the plans for a special heat-resisting metal I've invented," said Ted. "I expect you know that the fighting planes of the future can't go faster than a certain speed, because the metal starts to melt with the friction of the air. Well, I've solved the problem. Aircraft designers all over the world have been looking for a metal like this for years, and it's worth a lot to the country that can produce it."

Startled by the mysterious burst of flame behind him, the gunman half-turned. And that was Ted's chance to leap.

With a cry of surprise the intruder spun around, and in a split second Ted seized his chance and jumped on the gunman, knocking him down.

Ginger sent the Jeep racing over towards the two struggling men, and arrived just as Ted delivered a crisp knock-out punch.

"Crikey! What was all that about?" asked Ginger. "Who is he?"

"I don't know his name," replied Ted. "But he's employed

"He must have been following you in a car," said Ginger.

"I know. And I'll bet he was responsible for interfering with my engine and so forcing me to land," said Ted. "Look here, you said you were going to Midtown Bank, didn't you? Well, just for safety's sake, would you take my plans and have them put in the bank's safe?"

"All right," said Ginger doubtfully. "But . . ."

"In any case," grinned Ted. "You'd better have them in case

Ginger's way of helping the pilot to take off in such a small space was to stage an amazing tug-o'-war between the plane and the Super Jeep. No wonder the eyes of the hidden watcher popped.

Adventures

this little take-off trick of ours doesn't come off and I crash. Come on — let's get started."

Ginger tucked the envelope of plans safely into his inside pocket. Then he took a length of rope from the back of the Jeep, tied one end to the tail-skid of the aeroplane and the other end to the back axle of the Jeep.

"OK?" said Ted cheerfully.

"I hope this works out," gulped Ginger nervously.

The aircraft engine coughed once or twice and then burst into a roar. Ginger turned the cylinder on his Gasgun to where it said CUTTING GAS, and then climbed into his Jeep.

As Ted opened the throttle of his engine, Ginger edged forward the Jeep speed control. He twisted around in the driving seat and pointed the Gasgun at the taut rope behind him.

Louder and louder roared the aircraft's engine. The tail of the machine gradually lifted off the ground and the whole aircraft shook violently with the strain of trying to hurtle forward. But it couldn't move! The powerful green wheels of the Jeep were turning fast in the other direction and holding the plane.

Ginger had done some weird things with his Super Jeep, but never before had he had a tug-o'-war with an aeroplane!

It seemed that the propeller would tear the engine out of its mounting as it spun faster and faster. Then Ted raised his gloved hand and brought it down sharply.

That was the signal for Ginger to press the trigger of his Gasgun and at the same time shut off his speed control.

The rope parted with a loud twang and, as if shot from an aircraft carrier's catapult, the little plane flashed across the field and up into the air.

Ginger held his breath as the plane rocketed towards the trimmed trees, and then he heaved a sigh of relief as the machine safely cleared them.

"Phew! He made it!" breathed Ginger. "And now for Midtown Bank."

But as Ginger headed down the road for Midtown he didn't notice a thin man with close-cropped hair emerge from the bushes at the side of the road, drag a motor cycle from the ditch, and set off on Ginger's trail.

That evening Ginger was in his bedroom cleaning his Gasgun when he heard the clang-clang of a police car's bell. He saw the car pull up outside the Matthews' house.

Presently Mr Matthews hurried out of the house.

"But I don't think we can do anything about it," Mr Matthews was saying, struggling to put on his collar and tie. "The time-lock is set for ten o'clock tomorrow morning."

That was all Ginger heard before the manager got into the police car, but it was enough to make him get out his Super Jeep and set off after the car!

There was a large crowd around the bank in Midtown, and Ginger had never seen so many policemen before in all his life!

"Hullo again," cried a cheerful voice, which Ginger at once recognised as belonging to his pilot friend, Ted Johnson. "Looks like trouble keeps following me, doesn't it?"

"What's up?" asked Ginger.

"As far as I know they've had a burglar in the bank," said Ted. "He managed to open the safe door and got inside to look for something, and then it closed behind him. He's trapped!"

"Well, why don't they unlock the safe and cart him off to the cop-shop?" asked Ginger.

"The safe's got one of those time-locks," explained Ted. "It's been set for ten o'clock tomorrow morning and no keys will open it until then. By that time the burglar will probably be dead from lack of air. Unless, of course, another skilful burglar can open it up!"

"Would he be after your plans, do you think?" said Ginger.

"No, no," said Ted. "Impossible. You and the bank manager are the only ones who know my papers are there."

Before Ginger could reply, Mr Matthews came out of the bank.

"Oh dear, oh dear!" he said, when he saw Ginger. "I don't think even your wonderful cart can help us now. Even though the man is a crook we don't want him to suffocate. And if we try to burn the safe open, or use explosives, it will kill him anyway. I wish there was something we could do."

"Maybe there is," said Ginger, reaching for his Gasgun. "Can I go in?"

Thanks to Ginger being a friend of the manager he was admitted to the bank. Ginger went straight up to the big safe and spun the Gasgun cylinders around to DISSOLVING GAS again. Then he placed the nozzle of the gun a few inches away from the thick steel door of the safe and pressed the trigger.

A thin jet of blue smoke shot out and sizzled against the wall of steel, and the super-hard steel began to bubble and dissolve!

Gradually the jet ate into the steel, and Ginger moved the Gasgun round and round, cutting out a large chunk of the safe.

At last the chunk was cut away and it fell outwards as Ginger stepped back.

"There you are," said Ginger as the police moved forward.

But he noticed that the police were eyeing his Gasgun curiously.

Sure enough, the Midtown

"Stop that soap-box!" shouted the speed cops.

Inspector said: "Let me have a look at that, young man."

Ginger looked for a way to escape. He could see there was a possibility of the Gasgun being taken from him.

But at that moment a voice snapped:

"I'm a doctor. Let me see that man before you move him."

Thankful for the interruption Ginger slipped quickly out through the door and joined Ted.

"I'm off," he told Ted hurriedly. "The police have got their eye on this toy of mine."

"I'll come with you," said Ted. "But — Great Scot! Look!"

He pointed to the bank door, through which two hefty policemen were carrying the trembling burglar, followed by the doctor.

And the doctor was the sinister man who had held up Ted at pistol-point!

"It's him!" cried Ted. "And the burglar is his henchman!"

"After him," snapped Ginger. "I'll bet your plans are in the doctor's black bag."

But even while they were pushing their way through the crowd, the fake doctor had the burglar placed in the back of his powerful car and off he drove as if taking the burglar for treatment.

"The Jeep. Quick!" snapped Ginger, diving for his wonder cart.

Ted needed no second telling. Even as the green wheels started rolling he leapt behind Ginger.

"Hey! I want you!" roared a voice from the pavement. It was the police inspector.

Ginger's mind worked like lightning. Above all he wanted the police to follow him.

"Yah! Try and catch me, Flatfeet!" he yelled at the astonished inspector, and the next minute he was pleased to hear the clanging bell of a police car on his tail some way behind.

Meanwhile, the villain's car had a good lead, and Ginger crouched low as he sent the Jeep rocketing in pursuit.

"He's heading for the bridge over the river," yelled Ginger. "I know a short cut. Hang on!"

Ted hung on grimly and they fairly whistled along a country road leading to the river. Then to Ted's horror they headed for the side of a huge oil tank.

Handling the Jeep with confident skill, Ginger drove straight up the side of the tank, across the curved top and then out along two narrow pipes which carried oil from the tank to the oil refinery across the river.

The pipes were just wide enough for the wheels of the Jeep, and as Ginger risked a glance down he thanked his stars that the green wheels clung like limpets.

Down-river they could see the road bridge, and there was something speeding across it — it was the getaway car.

"He'll have to come this way," shouted Ginger, as they swooped straight down the refinery wall on to a road. "We'll lay an ambush."

He swung the Jeep into a side road and halted. The sound of the racing car drew nearer and nearer. Ginger unclipped his Gasgun and spun the cylinders around till ADHESIVE GAS came in line with the barrel.

He aimed the Gasgun's muzzle for the middle of the road and pressed the trigger. Nothing seemed to happen except for a faint hissing noise from the gun barrel. But as the car drew level with Ginger it suddenly halted as if grabbed by a mighty hand!

A stream of angry foreign language came from the car, and the villain jumped out. But as soon as his feet touched the road he stuck like a fly to a flypaper!

"That's him fixed," said Ginger grimly. "That Adhesive Gas will wear off in ten minutes but the police should be here before then."

"And I can give them plenty of evidence to prove that this character who posed as a doctor is working with that bank burglar lying in the back of the car, and that they've got papers belonging to me," said Ted.

"Then there's nothing else for me to do," said Ginger, "except get out of the way before that angry police inspector arrives!"

"All right, Ginger," laughed Ted. "Thanks for everything — including that hair-raising ride on your Jeep. But I'll stick to aeroplanes, I think. They're not half so frightening!"

But Ginger shot away after the crooks, faster than the police car could travel!

When it came to travelling in style, not to mention danger, this DANDY superstar's vehicle took a lot of beating. It sported two horns and neither of them made a sound.

During the late 1930s and early '40s there were many weird and wonderful stories in **Dandy** and **Beano**. Here are just a few of the daring deeds, hulking heroes and bizarre beasts from…

THE EARLY YEARS

One of the most popular adventures from that era was **Dandy's Little White Chief Of The Cherokees,** originally published in 1939. The opening two episodes appear on the following pages.

If you go down to the woods today you're in for a big surprise.

A real cliff-hanger of a story.

7 TERRIBLE TASKS FOR THE 7TH SON

If there's one thing worse than a frog in the throat it's a prince on the palate.

THE PRINCE ON THE FLYING HORSE

STRANG THE TERRIBLE

IN THE LAND OF THE SILVER DWARFS

Wait till Strang's wife sees what he won at the fairground.

JAK THE DRAGON-KILLER

Jak's a natty dresser in his snakeskin suit and it looks as if he has a bone to pick with someone.

RED HOOF

Looks like someone's heading the wrong way down a one-way street.

LITTLE WHITE CHIEF OF THE CHEROKEES

FAR out in the wastes of the American Prairie, a handful of settlers, men, women and children were making a desperate stand against a marauding horde of Cherokee Indians. The Redskins were galloping round the circle of big covered waggons in which the pioneers had crossed the great American plains. The air was filled with the rattle of rifle fire, the neighing of terrified horses, and the fierce war whoops of their Redskin riders. Suddenly, above the noise of the battle, there sounded a woman's voice, shrill with fear. "The waggons are on fire," she shouted. The Indians had made fire arrows and shot them into the canvas covers of the waggons. Within a few minutes four of the prairie schooners, as they were called, were blazing fiercely. But still the settlers kept on shooting. And amongst the bravest of the defenders was a fair-haired boy, firing from behind the wheel of a waggon. Behind the boy, whose name was Harry Martin, were his mother and sister, Nancy, busily reloading his rifles.

2 — Harry was on his way across the prairie with his mother and sister to meet his father, a gold prospector, who had made the journey west some months earlier. He had struck gold and had sent word for his family to join him. Now Harry was fighting so that his father might be able to see his family again. The boy was firing rapidly, and time after time his bullets were sending Indians plunging from their saddles. Harry kept up his fire as arrows thudded into the woodwork all around him.

3 — But the pioneers were losing the struggle, and already the Indians had broken through the circle of waggons at several points. Harry heard their triumphant cries as they closed with the pioneers in hand to hand battle. The boy flung down an empty rifle, and turned impatiently to his mother. "Quick, mother — another rifle!" But his mother shook her head. "That is the last of the ammunition, Harry," she cried. Harry sprang to his feet. "Then get into the waggon!" he yelled.

4 — His mother and sister clambered into the waggon, which was one of the few left unburned. Holding his rifle like a club, Harry prepared to defend them with his life. The warriors were sweeping through the waggons one by one and the exhausted settlers fell to the tomahawks and knives of the Cherokees. Two pioneers held them back for a few moments, fighting with bare fists against the armed attackers. Then they too fell, and the warriors came charging fiercely at young Harry.

5 — With all his strength, Harry crashed the butt of his rifle into the painted face of the foremost Indian. As the Cherokee went sprawling backwards amongst his fellows, Harry drew back his arms for another blow. The movement made his shirt open at the neck, and revealed the strange birthmark in the shape of a raven which the boy bore on his chest. When the Indians saw this, they fell back with gasps of awe. Harry gaped in bewilderment. Why had the warriors stopped their attack?

6 — The boy had picked up the Indian tongue from listening to the many peaceful Indians who worked in the many settlements in the East. "See, see, a white Hiawatha!" They brought a rough litter and signed to him to climb on it. Meanwhile, his mother and sister were allowed to remain unharmed in their waggon while horses were harnessed to it. Then the litter was carried off by four brawny braves till they came in sight of the wigwams of the great Cherokee tribe.

7 — There, a tall Indian came over to Harry. He told the boy he was War Eagle, Chief of the Cherokee Indians, and pointed to the tribal totem-pole, bearing a carved raven. "Why, that is just like the birthmark on my chest!" exclaimed the boy. War Eagle told how the pole had been given to his tribe centuries before by Hiawatha, greatest of all the Indian chiefs. "It is said in the legends of my people," went on the Cherokee, "that Hiawatha would send someone bearing his sign. You must be the one!"

8 — War Eagle beckoned to Harry to enter the chief's wigwam. But as the boy moved forward, a terrified scream suddenly rent the air. It was Harry's mother. She and Nancy had left their waggon, and when the boy turned, with his rifle still in his hand, he was in time to see his mother fling herself between little Nancy and a huge grizzly bear. Harry dashed forward at top speed to try to save her from the deadly attack of the fierce brute.

9 — The bear struck his mother to the ground with a flashing blow from its paw. But before the grizzly could strike again, Harry sprang in, and with all the strength in his shoulders, he smashed the butt of his gun into the beast's hairy face. The force of the blow cracked the butt. But the tremendous blow only angered the grizzly. The bear gave a loud growl and suddenly made a quick lunge forward towards the daring boy.

10 — It crashed Harry to the ground, and its paw was about to smash downwards when War Eagle came racing to the rescue. As he ran, he flung a stone tomahawk with deadly aim. It buried itself in the grizzly's throat. Fiercely, the bear tore at its throat with its paws, trying to claw the weapon out. But the axe-head was too deeply buried. Right above Harry the mighty beast stood tottering, with blood gushing from its wound.

11 — Then, with a crash, the bear thudded to the ground — dead! Harry helped his mother to her feet, and she and Nancy were taken to a wigwam to be cared for. That night Harry was led into the Council lodge, where the wise men of the tribe met. There, he was made Little White Chief of the Cherokees. Harry was bewildered. How would he and his mother and Nancy ever be able to reach his father in California now?

Y OUNG Harry Martin, the Little White Chief of the Cherokee Indians, lay beside his sister, Nancy, on the floor of a wigwam, while his mother gave an arithmetic lesson. The three of them had been on their way across the prairies to California to meet Harry's father, a gold prospector, when they had been captured by the Cherokee Indians. Harry's life had been spared and he had been made a Chief when the Redskins saw the strange birthmark on the boy's chest. It was shaped exactly like the carved raven on top of the tribal totem pole, given to the Cherokees centuries before by the famous Chief, Hiawatha.

2 — But Harry was worried, for the big wigwam of animal skins which was now their home was also their prison! Harry could have anything he cared to ask for — except his freedom! But meanwhile there was arithmetic to worry about. There had been a blackboard and chalk in the covered waggon which had brought them from the East, and now his mother gave Harry and Nancy an hour's lessons every morning. She was explaining a sum to them when suddenly her face filled with horror as she glanced up from the blackboard. "Look!" she screamed, pointing to a weird shadow which had fallen on the sunlit wigwam floor.

3 — It was a shadow with a horned head and menacing arms. Harry looked up at the door of the wigwam. There stood a strange figure, wearing a horned head-dress and a costume of feathers and gaudily-painted skins. Harry sighed with relief, for it was only the Medicine Man of the tribe. Then the Indian began to speak in the Indian tongue, which Harry knew almost as well as his own. "Hail, Little White Chief," he said. "The warriors of your people go to hunt buffalo. Come, and luck shall be with us."

4 — So it was that a little later Harry set off from the camp with the rest of the Indian braves, while the Medicine Man pranced about, going through the hunting rites of the tribe to the beat of an Indian drum. The Red men thought that, with Harry in the hunt, good fortune would be sure to follow their arrows. When they had gone some distance across the prairie, one of the scouts they had sent out brought back news that there was a big herd of buffalo only a short distance ahead.

5 — Each of the hunters carried a rolled-up buffalo skin at his saddle, and these were now spread across the backs of the horses, till, from a distance, the horses looked just like buffaloes. Then, hiding under the skins, the Indians began to approach the herd. Harry and the Red men got within arrow range without the mighty beasts suspecting anything. Suddenly the hunting cry of the Cherokees rang out. It was the signal to fire.

6 — Taking careful aim, Harry shot an arrow at the nearest buffalo. The barb buried itself in the thick fur round its neck and snorting with pain, the buffalo plunged about wildly, trying to get rid of the arrow. But its struggles grew weaker, until at length it sank to the ground. Harry had made his first kill! But he never saw the death of this buffalo, for by the this time the rest of the herd was stampeding all around him.

7 — Suddenly a daring idea for escape came to the boy. He would leap from the horse on to one of the buffaloes, and let it carry him away from the Red men. With a swift glance, Harry picked out the most powerful one of the herd. Next second, hands outstretched, he sprang from the back of his galloping horse. His fingers dug themselves into the buffalo's thick fur, and with a mighty effort, he got one leg over its back. Harry looked round desperately. On all sides were plunging, snorting buffaloes with horns lowered and tails erect. Suddenly an arrow came whizzing past Harry's head, and he realised that his buffalo formed the target for most of the Indian bows. Harry had chosen for his escape the King of the Prairies, the buffalo every Indian brave wanted to kill! For years this buffalo had defied the efforts of the most daring Indian hunters. It was said in the legends that it could never be killed, and that arrows broke on touching it. But this only made every Cherokee the keener to bring it down.

8 — Harry saw now that there was no chance of escaping. The thought flashed into his mind that when they found him trying to get away they might put him and his mother and sister to death. He must bring no danger to his mother. There was only one thing to do — he must kill the buffalo to which he clung! Harry drew his gleaming Indian hunting knife and, holding on grimly, plunged the blade into the brute's throat.

9 — The boy found he had struck at the deadliest spot. The great beast seemed to shudder in its stride. Then the King of the Prairies stumbled in its headlong charge, and plunged forward, flinging Harry from its back. Even as he hit the ground, Harry had sense enough to roll to the side, just in time to escape being crushed by the mighty mass of the falling buffalo. With a tremendous crash, the King Buffalo fell, inches from the boy.

10 — The buffaloes behind swerved away in alarm as they saw their leader come down. This saved Harry from being trodden under by the thundering hoofs of the other great beasts. Harry lay there, until he felt himself gripped by strong hands. "Are you hurt, O Little White Chief?" came the voice of War Eagle, the Cherokee leader. "No, I'm all right," grinned Harry. "What's happened to the buffalo?" They turned and saw the Indian braves gathered in awe round the dead buffalo.

11 — "The Little White Chief has killed the King of the Prairies!" the Indians gasped. "Where the weapons of the greatest hunters broke, his knife struck home. Truly he has been sent to us by Hiawatha himself." And lifting Harry on their shoulders, they carried him back to the cheering encampment, where his mother and sister were waiting, thankful for his safe return. Harry was still a prisoner, but he was also the Little White Chief of a mighty band of warriors.

Appropriately, for comics produced in Scotland, several of **Dandy** and **Beano's** best-loved swashbuckling adventures have been set there. And when the place is Scotland, the period just has to be The Jacobite Rising. During the first half of the 18th century the country was in turmoil with rebels loyal to Bonnie Prince Charlie battling the king's Redcoat troops.

Red Rory Of The Eagles and **Six Brands For Bonnie Prince Charlie** thrilled **Beano** readers, while the scenes above featured in the **Dandy** saga **Eastward Ho With Prince Charlie's Gold.**

Overleaf, you'll find the rip-roaring climax to **Six Brands For Bonnie Prince Charlie** from **Beano** of 1945.

SIX BRANDS FOR BONNIE PRINCE CHARLIE

1 — Red Fergie, the loyal Jacobite, and his young pal Coll MacDonald, were in the district of Fort Augustus, looking for the sixth brother of MacLean of Calgary in order to get the sixth clue to a treasure the MacLean had hidden. They wanted the treasure to help put Bonnie Prince Charlie on the throne. At a cottage on the shores of Loch Ness they had decided to stay for the night. The cottager wished them a hearty "Good-night" as the pair went upstairs to their bedroom.

2 — But the pair wouldn't have been so cheery if they had known what was at the back of the cottage owner's mind. Once they were upstairs the rogue darted outside and betrayed their presence to their worst enemies, the Redcoats. He led a party of them to the lonely cottage and pointed out the rooms where the unsuspecting pair were preparing for bed. The Redcoats drew their weapons and mounted the stairs to the bedroom. Red Fergie and Coll were completely unaware of their danger.

3 — It was only when the door flew open and several armed Redcoats leapt into the room that they realised the villainous cottager had betrayed them. Hampered by the bedclothes and without arms the pair were soon prisoners. It was useless to put up a fight. They were helpless. Fergie saw the cottager sneer with satisfaction as they were tied up. Helpless, they found themselves forced out of the cottage and marched down to the beach.

4 — The Redcoats forced them into a large rowing-boat there and manned the oars. They intended taking their prisoners to their fort at the end of the loch. But they reckoned without the help for the prisoners that was due from an unexpected quarter. Watching from behind a large boulder was Rory of the Axes, the man Red Fergie was looking for. A Jacobite himself, he was a bitter enemy of the Redcoats.

5 — Unsuspectingly the Redcoats pushed off from the shore and started rowing. Suddenly, however, a look of surprise crossed their faces. Rory of the Axe appeared on the beach with his large weapon tied to a length of rope. He started swinging the axe round his head until it fairly whistled through the air, then he let go. A howl of fear arose from the Redcoats in the boat.

6 — They tried to row faster to avoid the glittering axe, but they were too late. With a heavy thud the razor-sharp weapon, with all the power of Rory's strong arms behind it, buried itself deep in the wood of the rowing boat. Fergie and Coll gave a cry of joy. They had not expected help. They watched eagerly as Rory on the beach grasped the rope and pulled with all his strength.

7 — A yell of alarm escaped the Redcoats as the boat stopped making headway. Feverishly the oarsmen strained at the oars. One of the Redcoats jumped to the stern and tried to free the axe, but that was hopeless. It was buried deep in the wood. Rory had done his job well when he had thrown the axe. It would need more than one scared Redcoat to shift it. Coll's eyes shone with admiration as he watched Rory. The grinning Jacobite's muscles rippled as he pulled on the rope with all his strength. It was a tug of war between him and the Redcoat oarsmen — and Rory was winning! Slowly but surely the boat was being dragged to the shore. Suddenly, however, the strain on the boat became too great. With a splintering, tearing sound the stern of the boat was heaved off! The Redcoats gave a roar of fear as water rushed into the boat.

8 — Soon it was practically underwater. The Redcoats were unable to keep their balance and nerves in the sinking boat. They either fell or dived overboard into the water. It wasn't deep, but their clothes hampered them in the water. Coll and Fergie were in a worse plight. With their hands bound the pair were helpless. They went under. But Rory came to the rescue. In the confusion he reached the pair and grabbed them.

9 — With little or no effort he lifted the pair out of the water and tucked them under each arm. Then, with the howls of the spluttering Redcoats ringing in his ears, Rory walked briskly up the beach. They were soon deep in the hills and safe from any pursuit that the Redcoats might have started. Fergie was fairly sure that the Redcoats would not chase them after the ducking and the show of Rory's strength.

10 — Rory of the Axe took the pair to his cave hide-out. Soon they had a fire going and were seated round it drying their clothes. Then Fergie told the MacLean about the treasure and the six clues on Rory and his other five brothers' backs. "We've got five of the clues, Rory," Fergie told him, "and the last one's on your back. Will you show it to us?" Rory grinned and tugged at his shirt.

11 — A Jacobite himself, he was only too glad to help the cause. Quickly he pulled the shirt off. A gasp of surprise and horror came from the pair who had been eagerly waiting to see the last clue. Rory's back had been covered with black dye. The clue was blotted out! Red Fergie and Coll were speechless. The five clues they already had would be of no use without the sixth. Who had blotted it out?

1 — Red Fergie scrubbed and scrubbed and scrubbed but still the black dye hid the sixth and last clue to the treasure they were after. Coll MacDonald and Red Fergie had got the first five clues, but they were helpless without the last one, which Rory of the Axe's enemies had blotted out some time ago, believing it to be a lucky charm. Fergie wanted the treasure to help put Bonnie Prince Charlie on the throne.

2 — Rory of the Axe, a Jacobite himself, was quite willing to give him the last clue — but the dye covered it completely. With the aid of a mirror, Coll showed the Higlander the blot still on his back. Coll and Fergie had fought hard for the other clues and they didn't want to give up the treasure hunt now — but how were they going to get the last clue? It was a real problem.

3 — Rory fingered his chin thoughtfully and led Red Fergie and Coll out of the cave. Once outside he pointed to some distant hills. "There's an old witch lives in yonder hills," he murmured. "Maybe she could give us some concoction to take off the dye." Fergie nodded a little hopefully. Any slight chance was better than none at all. They set off towards the witch's cave. Rory, with his huge axe, led the way.

4 — They climbed hills, jumped streams and waded rivers until at last Rory stopped at the foot of an unscalable cliff. "Once we get up here," Rory announced, "we're practically at the witch's cave." As he spoke he carefully fastened a length of rope he always carried with him to the handle of his glittering, razor-sharp axe. Eagerly Fergie and Coll watched his preparations and stood back as he finished. They knew what he was about to do.

5 — Once, twice, three times, Rory swung his great axe round his head and then let go. Like a streak of light it whistled skywards and lodged itself at the top of the cliff face. Rory gave a sharp tug to make sure it had got a good hold. The axe held. Coll decided it was about his turn to help. "I'm the lightest," he announced. "I'll go up and make the rope secure for you two."

6 — Coll had lived a hard life in the bracing air of the Highlands and he was as fit as a fiddle. He found no difficulty in swarming up the rope to the top and climbing over the edge. Once at the top it was an easy matter for the boy to slacken and pull out the axe and fit the rope securely to a nearby tree. Once this was done he shouted for Fergie and Rory to climb up.

7 — That was an easy matter for the pair. Fergie went up first. Although small, the red haired Jacobite was as tough as the steel of his deadly rapier with which he had made a name for himself. There were few men who would be able to cross steel twice with this wizard swordsman. Once over the top, Fergie helped Coll give Rory a hand over the edge. Rory picked up his axe and led the way to a dark tunnel.

8 — At the mouth of the tunnel the three made torches and lit them before entering. It was pitch black inside and the torches cast flickering shadows on the cold, damp walls. It was an eerie place, and Coll felt cold shivers running up and down his spine. Even Red Fergie and Rory were just a trifle scared. At last the tunnel opened out into a large cave — even more terrifying.

9 — Bent over a steaming cauldron with a raven perched on her skinny shoulder stood the witch, the most evil-looking person Coll had ever seen. The young lad ducked behind Red Fergie as he stepped into the cave towards the witch. Beside him the look on Rory's face told that even he was not too happy either. Fergie drew a deep breath and coughed. It wasn't loud, but it was loud enough for the witch.

10 — Her ugly head jerked round and, in a high pitched cackling voice, she demanded what they wanted. Coll managed to tell her that they wanted the blot removed from Rory's back. Fergie handed a purse of money to the old witch. Her eye glittered as she grabbed this with her claw-like hand. Replying that she would try to remove the blot, she started fussing about with books and bottles, mixing this, stirring that.

11 — At long last the old hag motioned Rory to bend over a slab of rock. The brawny Highlander did as he was bid and watched a little uncertainly as the witch approached with a ladle of bubbling liquid from a huge steaming cauldron. Red Fergie and Coll watched breathlessly. Would the witch succeed? Exactly what the witch did Red Fergie and Coll did not know, but at length she stepped back.

12 — Success! Fergie and Coll nearly danced with glee as they scanned Rory's broad back. Plainly they saw the sixth clue, tattooed on his skin — the imprint of a man's foot with the figure 12 below it. That was all, but it meant a lot in the search for the treasure. "Well, we've got the six clues," Fergie said. "All we've got to do now is find out what they mean and we'll have won the treasure for Bonnie Prince Charlie!"

1 — The three Jacobite treasure-hunters, Red Fergie, Coll MacDonald and Rory of the Axe were well on the road to the treasure which they wanted for Bonnie Prince Charlie. MacLean of Calgary had found and hidden the treasure and, before he died, had tattooed six clues to it on the backs of his six sons. The treasure seekers had found the six clues after many adventures and were now in Calgary beside MacLean's cottage, the first clue.

2 — Red Fergie looked at the second clue, an oak with an outflung branch. They saw the oak nearby and this in turn directed them to twin mountain peaks in the distance. Soon the three were tramping through a narrow defile between the mountains. Rory of the Axe strode a little behind Fergie and Coll. Suddenly the brawny Highlander darted forward with his hand outstretched to grab Fergie and Coll. What had happened?

3 — He found himself with Coll on the ground and the huge figure of Rory on top of him. They were under an overhanging ledge and it wasn't until a huge boulder weighing many tons crashed into the narrow pass that Fergie realised that Rory had made that dive to save him and Coll being crushed to death. When the shower of rocks subsided they got up, dusting their clothes, and thanked Rory.

4 — Rory dismissed the thanks with a wave of his hand and nodded to the boulder. "How are we going to get past that now?" he asked. "It's too smooth to climb and it blocks the path completely." Rory was right. Except for a tiny gap at one corner there was no way past. Coll pointed to the gap a little doubtfully. "I could get through there," he said, "but it would be a tight squeeze for Rory."

5 — Fergie nodded thoughtfully. "It looks like the only way, though," he decided at last. "We'll have to try it." Coll got down on his hands and knees and wriggled through. He managed easily. Then went Red Fergie. It was a tight enough fit even for him, but he managed. When Rory started to come through it looked as though he would stick half-way. It took all Red Fergie's and Coll's strength to drag him through the narrow cleft.

6 — More than one sigh of relief escaped them when at last he got through. Once past the barrier the three marched once more up the narrow defile. It was Coll, in the lead, who noticed the Celtic cross and drew the others' attention to it. Quickly the excited treasure hunters strode up the rocky slope to the grave-stone and studied the inscription on the front. "It's the fourth clue ," said Fergie. "The treasure's getting nearer."

7 — The inscription on the tombstone told them the whereabouts of the treasure cave. It was on the banks of the loch nearby. Coll pointed to some cliffs on the other side of the loch. "Come on," he said, excitedly. "Let's find the cave." With quick steps because they knew they were nearing their goal, the treasure seekers hurried round the side of the loch. Three pairs of eager eyes searched for the cave as they went.

8 — Coll was a little in front and it was he who spotted the dark opening at the foot of the towering cliffs. He gave an excited yell to the two men behind him and darted forward to the mouth of the cave. But although Coll had forgotten the grim warning of the Ghost Wolf on the tombstone Red Fergie hadn't. "Stop!" he roared. "Don't forget the Ghost Wolf." Coll turned his head at the warning.

9 — That was the luckiest thing the boy did. Not looking where he was going, he didn't see the stone at his feet. He tripped over it and went sprawling — just a second before the jaws of the Ghost Wolf snapped shut just where Coll's throat should have been. The silent brute had leapt from the dark shadows of the cave at the unsuspecting boy. Its leap carried it over Coll, lying on the ground.

10 — Rory, however, was right behind him, and the brawny Highlander drew back his axe. The keen blade whistled through the air and bit deeply into the wolf's shoulder. The brute dropped dead at his feet. Coll picked himself up and managed a grin, although it hadn't been a very pleasant experience. Red Fergie led the way into the cave and started hunting around. He didn't have to hunt far. He found the last clue on a large rock.

11 — Thoughtfully Fergie studied the clue. "Man," he said at length. "I've a fancy the treasure's to be found not more than twelve feet from this spot." He looked around him at the bare rock. There didn't seem to be any hiding place for treasure. Suddenly, however, his eyes fell upon a ledge about 12 feet from the ground. The back of the ledge was hidden from view. "We'll form a pyramid and see what's on that ledge," he said.

12 — That was soon done, and it wasn't long before Coll peeped over the edge of the ledge. Then he nearly fell off Fergie's shoulders with glee. A sack full of glittering jewels lay within easy reach. Soon the boy had the sack down and emptied on the floor. Coll danced with glee, while Rory and Fergie clasped hands over their success. That treasure would be a great help to Bonnie Prince Charlie.

Flame and Fury — powerful golden eagles totally loyal to **Rory,** their young master. A boy and his birds — allies in the battle against the Redcoat foe. This dramatic tale appeared in **The Beano Book** of 1961.

RED RORY
OF THE EAGLES

THE SCOTTISH CONNECTION

On a snow-covered hillside in the Scottish Highlands, a strange hunt was taking place. A hare raced for its life, pursued by two great eagles and a sturdy boy wearing a kilt. The boy was Red Rory and the birds his trained eagles, Flame and Fury. It was the winter of 1746. The Jacobite Rebellion had failed and Rory was only one of many Jacobites who lived in the hills as outlaws, constantly hunted by the Redcoats.

The hare took refuge in a small cave. As Rory entered the cavern after the animal he found himself looking into the barrel of a pistol held by a Highlander with a bloodstained bandage on his leg.

The injured man limped forward and examined Rory keenly before lowering the pistol. "Be seated, lad. I welcome you as a friend," he said. "I am Hector the Strong. Roderick, the son of my chief, Black Donald, is held prisoner by the Redcoats in Drewer Castle, which was his home before the Rebellion. Now Black Donald is an outlaw with a price on his head and the Redcoats threaten to execute Roderick if Black Donald does not give himself up. 'Tis my task to rescue Roderick, but I stopped a musket ball in the leg when I escaped from a Redcoat patrol some miles back. Will you complete this mission for me, lad?"

Without hesitation, Rory agreed. Then Hector removed a big locket from around his own neck and gave it to Rory. "In the locket there is the secret of a hidden entrance to Drewer Castle. Good luck! And take care! The countryside is alive with Redcoats."

Rory set off immediately. He made steady progress across the snow-covered hills towards Drewer Castle until, suddenly, Flame and Fury let out warning screeches. A patrol of Redcoats topped a nearby ridge.

At once, Rory broke into a run. Shots and shouts from behind told the lad he had been spotted. Almost out of breath, Rory reached the edge of a frozen loch and pulled his targe from his shoulder. The Redcoats were closing in fast.

Swiftly, Rory slipped his feet through the thongs on the back of the shield and grabbed his eagles' legs.

A sharp cry sent Flame and Fury winging out over the ice, dragging Rory after them at high speed. The Redcoats were left far behind.

English cavalry patrolled the opposite shore of the loch. The Redcoats Rory had outwitted flashed a signal to them with mirrors.

The cavalrymen whipped up their horses and galloped to head the fugitive off.

Once across the loch, even the swift-footed Rory had little chance of outrunning horses. The thunder of hooves sounded louder in his ears as the cavalry spotted a herd of deer and a sharp order sent his eagles flashing towards them.

With talons bared, the screeching eagles swooped on the deer, driving them in blind terror down on the cavalry. Horses plunged madly, unseating their riders, and in the confusion Rory found it easy to escape.

It was dark when Rory halted some distance from Drewer Castle, which stood by the sea. Curious, he opened the locket, the inside of which carried a rough plan and bore a rhyme which ran —
'Neath the black rock by the keep,
The tunnel lies two fathoms deep.

Rory searched around until he saw a rock which was much darker in colour than the others. Then, fearlessly, the boy plunged into the sea.

Down, down went Rory until he spotted the black entrance to a tunnel in the rock face. The lad swam strongly into the dark cavern. He knew he was taking his life in his hands.

At last, Rory's bursting lungs forced him to strike upwards, and with a gasp of relief his head broke surface in a dark and gloomy cavern.

Stone steps led Rory to a little door set in a stout stone wall. Stones littered the floor. Rory picked up one to use as a weapon if need be.

The door opened on to a dark tunnel which led Rory by a maze of passages to the dungeons. A Redcoat jailer was on duty. With unerring aim, Rory hurled the stone at the jailer and struck the man down.

Roderick was the only prisoner in the dungeons. Swiftly, Rory took the jailer's key and released Roderick. "I am a friend," whispered Rory. "Follow me and keep quiet!"

The two lads were moving towards the secret entrance when, suddenly, there was a tremendous clanging noise behind them. The jailer had staggered to his feet and was sounding the alarm.

There was no need for caution now. Rory and Roderick ran all out for the secret tunnel. Suddenly, from ahead, they heard heavy boots ringing on the flagstones and the rattle of soldiers' equipment. Hunted and hounded, the fugitives were driven on to the high castle ramparts. There seemed no escape. Urgently, Rory called on Flame and Fury.

As the great eagles swooped down, Rory and Roderick each grasped the bird's legs and flung themselves into space. The eagles' beating wings and the soft snow broke their fall.

The night soon swallowed up the fugitives as they ran off, until in a nearby forest they were safe from pursuit. By daylight, they had reached the cave where the wounded Hector waited.

"Bravely done, lad," roared Hector, grasping Rory's hand warmly. "We can never repay you for this service. But any time you are in trouble, Hector the Strong is your friend." Rory watched Roderick and Hector as they set off across the hills to join Black Donald. The great adventure was over.

And now for something completely different — **Willie's Whizzer Broom** provided light-hearted adventure for **Dandy** readers in 1956.

WILLIE'S WHIZZER BROOM

ZOOM! Willie Meldrum sent his model plane flashing into the air. "What a beauty!" Willie gloated as he watched his plane's steady flight. Then came disaster. The plane suddenly dipped and crashed into the back of Major Prout's neck. "S-s-sorry, Major," Willie called. "It was an accident."

2 — "Accident!" bellowed the Major. "You did that deliberately." He charged towards Willie, brandishing his umbrella. But Willie dodged the Major. He picked up his plane and hopped astride his Whizzer Broom. *Whoosh!* At once the amazing broom whisked him off through time to the year 2500.

3 — Willie scarcely expected to find toy planes causing trouble in the wonderful world of the future. Yet the first thing he saw when he arrived was something like his own mishap. Three boys had broken a window with their wonder toy and the crash had attracted the police. "Scram!" gasped one boy.

4 — Willie stared at the plane in his own hand for a moment. "Wow!" he gasped. "If the cops see this they'll think I broke the window. I'd better hop it, too." So Willie joined the three boys on the run. Hard though they tried to shake the cops off their trail, however, they couldn't manage it. "I'm done for," Willie finally panted. "I can't run any more. We'll have to stop those cops." And he loaded his plane with stink bombs.

5 — How those cops panicked when the plane zoomed, upside-down, above their heads. *Crunch! Tinkle!* The stink bombs showered down around them and they panicked even more. Nothing in this world of the future was allowed to make a smell, and the horrible pong from the stink bombs really scared the cops. "Help!" gasped the one with the moustache. "I'm being gassed. Call out the Sanitary Squad at once."

6 — The other cop charged along to the corner and pressed an alarm switch set in the wall. Within seconds there came the wail of sirens and the Sanitary Squad arrived. Lumbering around in their strange protective clothing, they sprayed special Anti-Germ Foam on the stink bombs and shovelled the frothy mess into containers. Willie laughed until his sides were sore. "All that trouble to deal with stink bombs!" he chortled. His new pals were very grateful to Willie for helping them to escape.

7 — "Here you are. Take this," one of the lads said, thrusting his super plane into Willie's hands and then running after his pals. "Coo!" gasped Willie. "What a whopper! I bet I have fun with this." But, unknown to Willie, the two cops had found something which was going to land him in lots of trouble. It was a stink bomb which hadn't burst. "You hold it while I examine it," the whiskery cop told his companion. Gingerly the other cop held up the bomb for Whiskers to examine.

8 — "Aha!" grunted Whiskers. "Fingerprints! Now we'll soon find out who owns this, and that'll tell us who our attacker was." Off to the Police Headquarters tramped the cops, and here they put the stink bomb in an amazing machine. A strange lens floating above the stink bomb photographed the finger-prints on it and at once a complicated set of machines went to work, trying to find fingerprints in the police files which were exactly the same as the ones showing up on the stink bomb.

9 — But no citizen's number flashed on the screen. The machine was beaten, and the cops were baffled. "The machine must be broken," growled the whiskery sergeant. "We have every citizen's fingerprints in our files. There's nobody we haven't fingerprinted." "Just a minute," broke in the other sergeant. "What about that strangely-dressed boy who keeps appearing and causing so much trouble?" Willie had been rumbled! In a few minutes he was surrounded by policemen.

10 — Willie stood no chance. He was lassoed, trussed up and carted off to Police Headquarters. "Now," demanded the whiskery sergeant. "You attacked us, didn't you? Own up!" Willie said nothing. "Very well! Put him in the chair, men," the sergeant commanded.

11 — The cops hastened to obey, clamping Willie into a padded chair and fixing an odd helmet on his head. "This is a mind reading machine you're seated at," the sergeant informed him. "Since you won't admit your crime, we're taking steps to prove it." He stamped on the pedals in front of the chair, pressed several switches, and with a deep hum the machine came into operation. Four screens flickered for a moment, then pictures flashed on to them. The machine had read Willie's memory and was showing some of the ways he had broken the law during his visits to the future!

12 — "I thought so!" the sergeant growled. "You're guilty. Six months of corrective training for you, my lad." Willie gasped. "You can't do that!" he shouted. "Can't I?" growled the sergeant. "Come here till I search you." And he emptied one of Willie's pockets.

13 — Willie grinned to himself. "Just wait till he sticks his hand in my other pocket," he thought. He didn't have long to wait. The sergeant dug deep into the pocket — then leapt high in the air. He'd sprung a mouse-trap which Willie had been taking home to Grandma!

14 — Before the sergeant had the trap off his finger Willie whizzed home with his new plane. "It's a topper!" he chortled as he watched it soar along. Then his grin faded and he got ready to run. His plane had cut Major Prout's hat in two. What a day of calamity!

Adventures

WILLIE MELDRUM groaned as he gazed at his homework. "That teacher has a nerve giving us sums like these. I'd need an adding machine to do them." Then Willie's frown vanished. "An adding machine!" he whooped. "That's it! I'll bet I can get one in 2500."

2 — Grabbing up a broom which was propped against the wall, Willie sat astride it and pressed a secret stud in the handle. At once there was a loud *WHOOSH!* and Willie vanished from the room. His Whizzer Broom was taking him to the wonderful world of the year 2500.

3 — When Willie landed in the future the first thing he saw was a school. "They ought to have at least one adding machine in there," Willie decided. "I'll take a look." But unknown to Willie, a cop of the future was deciding to take a closer look at this boy who had come zooming down from the sky.

4 — Willie was lucky. He saw an adding machine in a classroom and he nipped in through the open window. But there his luck ended. "Aw!" he moaned. "I've forgotten my exercise book." There was only one thing to do — take the adding machine back to 1956 with him.

5 — But that cop was still on his trail. By the time Willie had unscrewed the machine from its place on the floor and slung it under his broom, the cop was creeping up behind him. Then, *Whoosh!* As Willie soared away the cop made a dive at him and just managed to grab the machine.

6 — Of course that made no difference to the Whizzer Broom. It still carried Willie back to 1956, and it took the copper, too! Willie knew nothing of his passenger until he made a very soft landing. It was a soft landing because he came down on top of poor Sergeant Zol, the cop from the future!

7 — "How did he get here?" Willie wondered. But Sergeant Zol was rising so Willie hopped it, only inches ahead of Zol's outstretched hands. The sight of the oddly-dressed Sergeant Zol chasing a schoolboy, however, brought a 1956 bobby along at the double.

8 — "Hoi!" he yelled to Zol. "Leave that boy alone. Stop in the name of the law." Sergeant Zol stopped. "What?" he roared. "*I am* the law!" He pointed a gloved hand at the bobby and, *ZIP! CRACKLE!* Sparks flew from the tips of his glove towards the bobby.

9 — At once the bobby jerked to a standstill and collapsed, stiff as a board. Sergeant Zol's Paralysing Ray Glove had made short work of him. "Now I can get after that young thief," he growled, snapping handcuffs on the helpless bobby. "Come on, you."

10 — Zol tied a rope round the bobby's waist and, with his dazed prisoner in tow, went looking for Willie. He couldn't see Willie anywhere, but he did see two more bobbies standing on the corner of the street. His eyes blazed at the sight of the blue uniforms.

11 — One man in blue had already attacked him and ruined his chances of catching Willie, so Sergeant Zol reckoned that if one of these men was a criminal, all men in this uniform were criminals. "Well, I'm not going to give them the chance to attack me," he muttered. "I'll arrest them first." Before the two bobbies knew what was happening they were flattened by a couple of mighty blows from Zol's fist. The cop from the future hadn't even time to handcuff his latest prisoners when there was an angry shout and two more bobbies charged towards him.

12 — "This place is over-run with criminals," Zol grunted. "I wonder where the police are?" The last two bobbies who ran up to arrest the cop from the future had as little success as the first three. *ZONK! CLONK!* Sergeant Zol laid them out as quick as winking and promptly roped the whole lot together. "Perhaps I can settle down to catching that young rogue now," he muttered and, dragging the bunch of dazed bobbies, he went looking for Willie. He didn't have far to look, because Willie popped his head round a corner and made a face at him. Zol roared angrily.

13 — He charged round the corner — right into Willie's trap! The crafty lad whipped the top off a coal hole right in Zol's path. Down went the cop from the future, dragging the dazed bobbies with him. At once Willie clapped the lid back on the coal-hole.

14 — "Now to do my sums," Willie chortled. That machine from the future certainly was a fast worker. In five minutes it solved all Willie's problems. Pleased as could be, he zoomed off to the future with it. Then all of a sudden he remembered that he had left Sergeant Zol in the cellar!

15 — Back to 1956 he went to drag the cop from the future out from beneath the dazed bobbies. Then he made another trip to the future to take Sergeant Zol home. Dumped beside the adding machine, the dazed cop was left wondering if he had imagined it all.

16 — Next day the teacher had just told Willie how good his homework was when five angry bobbies arrived. "Oh-oh! Trouble!" Willie muttered. He was right. And when the bobbies had finished with him Willie wished he'd left his sums undone and faced the wrath of his teacher!

Adventures

'Young Frankie' may sound like a very familiar way of referring to one of England's greatest heroes, but that's how the young Sir Francis Drake was known in this tale from The Dandy Book of 1954. Fictional episodes from the legendary mariner's boyhood also appeared in the weekly comic during the same year.

YOUNG FRANKIE DRAKE

SCARCELY a breath of wind rippled the surface of the English Channel as a rowing boat put out from Plymouth Harbour. Manning the oars was a stockily-built boy called Francis Drake, the self-same Francis Drake who in later years was to play such a great part in the defeat of the mighty Spanish Armada. But there was no thought of wars or of fighting in the mind of young Frankie on this autumn morn. He was going fishing, and two miles off-shore he shipped his oars and cast his lines overboard.

2 — As the morning wore on a fog came swirling up-channel. Frankie went on tending his lines. He could always tell by the flow of the tide where the shore lay. But with the fog, came sudden danger. Frankie heard the creak of spars and the slap of canvas. Somewhere nearby there was a ship. It came looming out of the fog to starboard. There was no time to row clear, no time to shout for help before the row-boat was crushed like an eggshell. All young Frankie could do was leap upwards, groping blindly, despairingly, for a rope dangling from the great galleon's bowsprit.

3 — Frankie just managed to get his fingertips round the rope, and there he hung, like a spider on a thread, under the very noses of the enemy! For it was a Spanish ship that had run him down. Frankie saw that at a glance, and his pulse quickened as, hand over hand, he swung inwards to the ship's side. What could one boy do against a shipload of the dreaded Dons? When Frankie reached the ship's side he heard voices coming from a cabin. Cautiously he looked inside. He gasped. An English peasant was standing there amongst a crowd of bearded Spanish officers.

4 — But as Frankie watched, one of the Spaniards started dressing himself in a home-spun smock such as a yeoman farmer would wear. Then Frankie realised what was happening. These men were dressing up to look like Englishmen. They were spies. Taking advantage of the fog, this galleon was going to put them ashore on some lonely beach. Quickly Frankie ducked out of sight and crawled through a gun port on to the lower gun deck. There was no one here. He cast off the ropes holding one of the cannons and heaved and strained to drag it from its port.

5 — Frankie took no thought of his own danger — his one concern was to have a tilt at the hated Spaniards. Already a plan had formed in his head. He manhandled the gun till he had it in the middle of the deck. Then he chocked up the rear of the gun carriage so that the muzzle was pointing downwards. That done, he primed and loaded the gun. But what now? Frankie lacked flint and tinder to fire the gun. Stealthily the boy crept up the nearest companion ladder. Ahead lay the fo'c'sle, and sitting there were some men smoking pipes and playing cards around a barrel.

6 — This was the first time Frankie had ever seen a pipe, although he had heard talk of such things amongst the seafaring men of Plymouth. He certainly knew that the bowl was full of burning leaves — the very thing to apply to the touch-hole of a gun. Frankie Drake did not hesitate. The galleon was nearing the shore, so there was no time to waste if the Dons' plan were to be foiled. He darted in through the doorway, snatched the pipe from the mouth of one of the startled Spaniards, then went racing back towards the ladder as fast as his young legs would carry him.

7 — After him pounded the Dons. From all over the ship they came, swarming down the ladder after the daring English boy. But Frankie kept his lead, and even puffed at the pipe as he ran to keep the tobacco aglow. As he reached the gun a dagger flashed through the air. It stuck quivering in the mast, pinning Frankie by the shirt. Fortunately, the dagger barely scratched Frankie's shoulder, and, undaunted, he shook the pipe over the touch-hole of the gun. *Boom!* The whole ship quivered as the gun roared and the cannon ball went ripping, tearing downwards. Splintering timber flew in all directions, and shrieking, screaming Spaniards went down like ninepins.

8 — A second later another explosion rocked the galleon. The cannon ball had hit some powder barrels and they exploded, ripping a huge hole below the water line. The galleon keeled over at a crazy angle, and sent screaming Spaniards and rumbling cannon balls careering helter-skelter across the deck. Acrid powder fumes clouded the air, and in the confusion Frankie Drake was forgotten. Quickly wrenching out the dagger, he scrambled up the sloping deck and plunged from a gun port into the sea. He came to the surface amid a litter of wreckage and boats packed with dazed Dons.

9 — As Frankie swam clear of the sinking ship he saw an empty boat bobbing about ahead of him. It had been thrown clear as the ship keeled over, and, though tangled with wreckage, it was undamaged. Frankie climbed aboard and took possession of it. By now a breeze had got up, to blow away the fog and reveal the sinking galleon to the whole of startled Plymouth. Launches put out from the shore to take the Spaniards prisoner, and Frankie, scudding along in the freshening breeze, led the way back to harbour. Francis Drake had struck his first blow for England.

Samson the Strongman, Danny the young acrobat, Trixie the trick rider, Gloopy the clown and Horace the educated ape . . . the cast of **The Shipwrecked Circus,** castaways on Coral Island since their ship was caught in a fierce tropical storm.
But this was no holiday! Their island home was neither lonely nor peaceful. In the story overleaf from **Beano** of 1955, the circus folk were joined by Jim Silver, a bearded old sailor who'd been washed ashore, and Old Jim wasn't Coral Island's only visitor . . .

"KEEP back, ye scum! I'm takin' charge o' these pearls!" The rasping voice of Skipper Barna of the schooner Cormorant was full of menace. Samson, Jim Silver and the other chums of the Shipwrecked Circus backed from the pistol in Barna's hand as he stepped into his boat waiting near the silver beach of Coral Island. The evil skipper clutched in his free hand a small bundle which contained a fortune in pearls — by rights Jim Silver's pearls. Jim was an old sailor who had come to the South Seas to seek a rich pearl-bed. Helped by the chums, Jim's search had been successful. Barna, a rascally trader, had got wind of the pearls and landed on the island.

2 — At pistol point Barna had forced the chums to hand over the pearls. Jim Silver was fuming with silent rage. But he and the chums could only watch helplessly as the ruffian was rowed by three of his cut-throat crew out to his schooner anchored in the bay. Suddenly Samson snapped his fingers. "Back to the hut, chums," he said quickly. "Danny, get out the frogman suit. Hurry! We've got to work fast. The schooner'll be pulling out in a minute." The chums raced to their small bamboo hut further along the beach and there they opened a sea-chest in which was carefully stored a complete frogman's outfit. The chums helped Samson to don the gear.

3 — In a few moments the strong-man was ready. "Right!" said Samson. "Don't say goodbye to your pearls yet, Jim. Now, listen carefully." Samson spoke quickly for a few minutes to the eager chums. Then he made his way out of the back entrance of the hut and, hidden from the schooner by jungle shrubs, headed for a small headland. There Samson quickly adjusted his headpiece and plunged into the warm waters of the bay.

4 — Through the green depths the strong-man swam, and not a ripple showed on the surface to arouse the suspicions of the look-out on the ship. Then through the clear water Samson saw the Cormorant's anchor chain. He was in time. With one powerful wrench, the strong-man snapped the chain off near the anchor. Then Samson felt a sudden tug at his leg. The tentacle of an octopus had wrapped itself round his ankle!

5 — In an ominous swirl of water a huge octopus glided out of a clump of water weed and Samson was caught in its powerful arms. He struggled like a tiger as he was dragged towards the ugly beak-like mouth. But his presence of mind saved him, for he had kept hold of the anchor. With a great effort Samson drove one of the flukes into the monster's rubbery body.

6 — Next moment the octopus's grip slackened and Samson squirmed free. With arms swirling the brute drifted into the depths, leaving a trail of blood behind it. Samson watched it go, rubbing his chafed limbs where the tentacles had gripped him. Then he glided to the dangling anchor chain. Grasping it firmly he began to pull the Cormorant towards the shore.

7 — It was several moments before Skipper Barna and his men noticed the motion of the schooner as it glided slowly and steadily towards the beach. Under the water, Samson plodded on, moving quicker now with the ship well under way. Then his head broke the surface as he reached the shallows — and the seamen saw him. But before their shocked amazement was over the ship grounded and lurched violently to starboard.

8 — The cut-throats panicked and leaped into the sea as Samson heaved the ship right to the water's edge. It was a colossal feat of strength! Samson whipped off the face mask as the chums joined him ready to deal with the crew. Samson scanned the sloping deck. Where was Karl Barna? No one saw a swirl of water near the stern of the ship. It was Barna swimming out of a secret trapdoor near the schooner's keel.

9 — The thieving skipper held a knife in his teeth and, fixed to his belt, was the precious bundle of pearls. He began to swim underwater towards Coral Island. At that very moment the chums were "welcoming" the Cormorant's ruffians ashore. The circus folk had armed themselves with heavy sticks and watched the bedraggled seamen come ashore. "Easy with these clubs," whined the bosun. "We had to obey the skipper!"

10 — Samson paid no heed to the crew as the angry Jim Silver escorted them to the beach hut. There was still no sign of Karl Barna. Suddenly young Trixie, the circus trick-rider, heard a faint splash in the sea behind her. Before she could move the fat figure of Barna rose out of the water and grasped her arm in a cruel grip. At the same time, his knife gleamed in the sunlight as he brought it close to the girl's back.

11 — "Stand back, ye dog!" snarled Barna as Samson moved towards him menacingly. "Stand back or I'll kill the girl." Samson had no choice. "Start walkin'!" said Barna to Trixie. "We're goin' to find a native canoe. I aim to leave this island — with these here pearls! You others take one step after me and ye know what'll happen!" At the knife-point Trixie was forced down the path that led along the high cliffs of Coral Island. Samson and the others watched in helpless anger.

12 — Below Barna and Trixie was a sheer drop of fifty feet into the sea, and the ruffian relaxed his grip. Trixie wouldn't try to escape in such a dangerous spot. But he reckoned without the cool courage of the girl. She suddenly broke from his grasp and daringly sprang off the cliff path. Fifty feet below she hit the water with a big splash, but unharmed. Immediately a powerful current caught the girl in its grip. She gasped with horror. Trixie had leaped into a dangerous whirlpool.

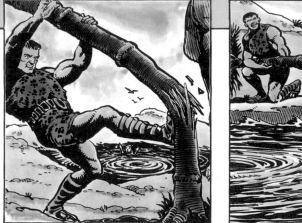

SAMSON's great muscles bulged as he heaved on a palm tree, trying to snap the trunk. The strong-man's face was grim, for upon his strength depended the life of Trixie, the young trick-rider of the Shipwrecked Circus. Trixie was caught in the swirling current of a whirlpool at the foot of the tall cliffs of Coral Island, the South Seas home of the circus chums. She had jumped from the cliffs to escape from Skipper Barna, the evil schooner captain, who was holding her as a hostage. Barna was making his getaway with a bag of pearls — the property of Jim Silver — and the trader had kidnapped Trixie and threatened to kill her if Samson followed him.

2 — With a rending crack, Samson snapped off the palm and raced with it to the whirlpool. There Danny, the acrobat, was waiting. At a signal from Samson he sat astride the tree trunk and took firm hold as Samson swung the tree out over the dangerous waters. Then when Trixie was swirled round towards him, she grabbed Danny's wrist and hung on. The plucky girl was swung to safety as Samson brought the tree back over dry land. Trixie was none the worse for her experience. Soon she was on her feet and following her chums in pursuit of the evil Barna. Along the cliff path the chums raced, watching the fat figure waddling up the slope of Fire Mountain.

3 — Fire Mountain was a volcano, always smoking ominously, but it had not erupted for many years. Barna was on his way over the hills to seek a native village where he could find a canoe and leave the island. As he moved quicker up the slope, Samson began to overtake him. Soon only the crater of the volcano separated him and the thieving Karl Barna.

4 — Barna's face went white with fear as he saw the grim look on Samson's face. He turned to run down the opposite slope, but he knew Samson would catch him. The strong-man had only to cross the crater. Suddenly, in a searing blast of fire, the earth rose at Samson's feet and the whole mountain trembled to a muffled roar in its interior. Fire Mountain was in eruption!

5 — "Get back!" gasped Samson to the chums. "Back down the mountain!" The circus folk raced for their lives as boiling lava bubbled from the fiery crater and began to trickle down the slope. For the moment Karl Barna was forgotten, and dense clouds of smoke and leaping flames hid the spot where he had last been seen. Perhaps he had been killed in the eruption. If that was the case, the ruffian would have got no more than he deserved.

6 — But what of the pearls? As the chums reached the safety of the jungle they became anxious for Jim Silver's lost fortune. But the pearls were still in the possession of the thieving trader, who was very much alive. He had escaped from the volcano by the skin of his teeth and now he, too, was in the jungle on the other side of the island, munching greedily at some juicy fruits which he had cut from the trees with his knife.

7 — Barna stuck his knife in a tree root and forgot about it as he took out some of the gleaming pearls. "Worth half a million quid," he chuckled hoarsely. The ruffian paid no heed to the chattering of monkeys in the trees about him. It was one of the usual noises of the jungle. Nor did he notice one of the monkeys creep towards his knife, snatch it, and scamper into the trees again. Barna went on gazing at the pearls, unaware that very soon his own knife would be the means of the circus chums finding him and trying to regain their stolen property.

8 — The bright gleam of the steel had attracted the monkey's attention and it thrust the blade between its teeth and began to swing through the trees, happy with its strange new possession. The other monkeys followed playfully trying to steal the knife. The little animals travelled far in a short time and as it happened they crossed the trail by which the chums were gloomily returning to their hut. It was Danny who spotted the glittering knife. He recognised it immediately. "Fetch that knife, Horace," he cried, ordering the clever circus ape into the trees.

9 — The chums watched Horace excitedly. Soon the ape grabbed the knife and was chattering away quickly to the little monkey. Horace was top of the class where educated apes were concerned. He soon made the monkey understand that he wanted to know where it had picked up the knife. The little animal dropped to the ground and went scurrying on all fours. After it bounded Horace and the other circus chums, tensed for action.

10 — It was plain now to Samson that Barna had escaped from the slopes of Fire Mountain. They could still hear the volcano rumbling in the distance, but already it was growing fainter as the eruption died down. Along winding trails and across others scampered the monkey. Then all at once it stopped, and ahead Samson caught sight of a striped jersey among the trees — Karl Barna. With a low growl the strong-man hurled himself forward.

11 — Barna gave a yell of fear as Samson's great weight crashed him to the ground. But with all the breath knocked out of his body, he still kept hold of the bag of pearls. As Samson towered over him, reaching down for the pearls, the rascal sighted the gleam of water nearby where Crocodile River ran to the sea. With an effort, Barna hurled the pearls towards the river.

12 — "Get the pearls now — if you can!" yelled Barna hoarsely. Samson dashed to the bank of the river. The pearls dropped with a plop into the water and began to sink, and Samson began to wade into the river, watching the blurred shape of the bag. Then he stopped abruptly. The long sinister shape of a crocodile was moving through the depths to investigate the little bag.

Adventures

LIKE a wrestler advancing, Samson, the strong-man of the Shipwrecked Circus, moved into Crocodile River on Coral Island to come to grips with his enemy — a huge crocodile that wallowed on the surface of the water. A small cloth bag was impaled on one of the monster's teeth. That bag contained a fortune in pearls, the property of old Jim Silver, the sailor friend of the Circus chums. The pearls had been stolen by Karl Barna, the ruthless skipper of the Cormorant, a South Seas trading schooner. Samson had tracked Barna down, and in desperation the rogue had hurled the bag of pearls into the river, where the croc had seized it in its jaws.

2 — Motionless as a floating log, the big crocodile eyed Samson carefully. Then with a sudden flick of its tail the reptile hurled itself to the attack. The battle of the giants had begun! Watching from the river bank, Barna saw the contestants vanish in a cloud of spray. When it cleared, Samson's left hand had closed in an unbreakable grip on the croc's snout. The other was grasping one scaly foreleg. The strong-man was careful not to try to snatch away the impaled bag. To do so might have torn the fabric and scattered the pearls over the river bed. There was only one thing to do, and with a great heave, he lifted the huge crocodile right out of the water.

3 — Barna's eyes popped — Samson was actually carrying the struggling croc ashore. With his fat legs trembling the rogue raced away into the bushes. Samson heaved the croc on the bank and his muscles swelled as he began to force open the huge jaws. "Gloopy!" gasped Samson. "Here — quick." From the group of circus chums watching nearby a little clown darted forward. "The pearls!" panted Samson. "Grab 'em!"

4 — Gingerly, Gloopy stretched a hand into the gaping jaws, reaching for the little brown bag. The croc grunted as it strained to close its mouth, but not an inch did the jaws move, such was the power of Samson's grip. Then, all at once, Karl Barna rose from the bushes and hurled a lump of rock full at Samson's head. The strong-man keeled over and the great jaws snapped shut, missing little Gloopy's hand by inches.

5 — Karl Barna laughed hoarsely as the croc turned and slithered into the water, the pearl bag still stuck in its jaws. "I'll get these pearls somehow," he muttered. Meanwhile, the other circus chums had raced to Samson's side. The strong-man was stunned, but Barna did not want to be around when he recovered. He raced away into the jungle at top speed.

6 — "Samson'll be as right as rain in a few minutes," announced Trixie, the girl trick-rider, as she bathed the huge bruise on the strong-man's head. An excited shout from Danny made the others jump to their feet. "The pearls! I've spotted 'em!" Danny led the way to a high part of the river bank and from there they looked down on a small islet.

7 — It was one of the sacred pools of the local natives. In the middle of the pool a tall grotesque totem-pole had been erected. The big croc was basking on the rock and a few feet from its jaws lay the bag of pearls, unstuck at last from the sharp teeth! The chums held a whispered conference and soon decided what they had to do. Danny fetched a rope from their jungle hut and quickly noosed it. Then, taking careful aim, he hurled the lariat out towards the totem on the rock.

8 — The noose caught round one of the long "arms" of the totem and Danny pulled it tight. "Right, Horace!" he said quickly. "It's up to you now." During this time, Horace the Educated Ape of the circus had removed his dusty shoes and spats. Now he took the end of the rope in his hands, and kicking off with his feet, leaped out over the river. Whoosh! Like a big pendulum the chimp swung past the rock and as he did so his dangling feet picked up the bag of pearls.

9 — The startled croc lunged forward, but its jaws snapped on the empty air. In a great arc, Gloopy swung to the other side of the river. As he did so, Karl Barna leaned out from behind a bush and snatched the pearl bag again! It had been done so quickly that Horace forgot to let go the rope and the jaws of the angry crocodile nearly got him on the back swing.

10 — The watching chums stared in silent anger as Barna pelted away down to the distant beach. Horace the ape had now safely landed on the far bank and he fairly danced with rage. "What's going on here?" boomed a deep voice from along the river bank. Samson had recovered from the cruel blow and the chums raced to tell him of Barna's cunning theft.

11 — The chums could see that Barna was heading for the Cormorant, which lay grounded just off-shore, her masts tilting over. That had been Samson's doing, for with a colossal feat of strength he had pulled the vessel into the shallows to prevent Barna's escape from the island. "Come on, chums," snapped Samson, on his feet now. They crossed the river by stepping stones and pelted down to the beach. Already Barna had scrambled on board and now he was launching a small boat.

12 — The boat had been lying upside down on the sloping deck, but fear of Samson gave Barna enough strength to drag the boat across the deck and fairly hurl it into the water. The chums raced right to the water's edge and Samson's fists clenched with anger. It seemed that Barna had outwitted them, for as they watched he swiftly hoisted sail on the boat and it scudded swiftly out to sea. Then his jeering voice rang out across the waves — "Ye can say goodbye to your pearls now!"

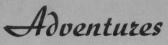

"HANG on, chums! Here we go!" the deep voice of Samson the circus strong-man boomed out as he braced himself against a sleek trading schooner that lay grounded in the shallows off Coral Island. Samson was attempting to push the vessel out into deeper water. She was the Cormorant, owned by an evil trader named Karl Barna. When Jim Silver, an old sailor friend of the circus folk, had found a rich pearl bed near the island, Karl Barna had got wind of the discovery. He brought his ship to Coral Island, and stole the

pearls. Samson had tried to thwart his getaway by running the Cormorant aground, but the cunning rogue had made his escape in a small sailing boat, while his crew of cut-throats had run off into the thick jungle. At that moment he was somewhere on the high seas and now the chums were going to take up the chase in the Cormorant. The powerful Samson pushed the ship through the shallows. Then at last she was rolling freely in deep water. Only a trickle of water came in through the planks which had scraped ground.

2 — Samson knew a bit about seamanship and when he pulled himself over the bulwarks, he set the chums to preparing the ship for sea. Quickly the wide white sails were unfurled, and Samson himself took the helm. The warm wind filled the sails as the Cormorant headed north, gliding along at a brisk pace. Old Jim Silver was left on the island, for a sudden bout of fever had struck him down. Now he lay resting in the chums' hut. An hour's sailing brought the chums their reward and it was Horace the ape who first saw the flash of a red sail on the horizon.

3 — It was Karl Barna's sailing boat scudding along to the islands to the north. But the Cormorant was swifter and began to overtake Barna's boat rapidly, helped by the rising wind. Samson looked anxiously at the darkening sky. A fierce storm was blowing up and the waves began to rise, the wind whisking spray from their crests. But it was a southerly gale and the Cormorant leapt forward under the force of it. In a matter of minutes, she closed with the sailboat and the chums saw the look of fury on Barna's face as he watched their approach.

4 — As the sailboat bumped along the side of the Cormorant, Barna seized a boat-hook and raised it, ready to defend himself. Samson left the tiller and ran to deal with the rogue. But the cunning Barna acted swiftly. He jabbed his boat-hook up at Gloopy, the dwarf clown, and the hook caught in the little chap's braces. Quickly Barna heaved him into the sea.

5 — Quick as a flash the fat trader leaned down and pulled the spluttering clown out of the water. The next moment, Gloopy felt the deadly point of the boat-hook prick his throat and heard Barna's rasping voice as he looked defiantly at Samson. "Keep away from me!" he rasped. "Go on, get back to your island or I'll fix your little pal for good!"

6 — Lightning flickered among the dark clouds as Barna drew back his boat-hook to strike. Then, with a shriek, a violent gust of wind swept the two vessels. The boom of the sailboat swung round and struck Barna full in the face. The quick-witted Gloopy threw himself down in the nick of time and found himself staring at the bag of pearls lying in the stern of the boat.

7 — Gloopy picked up the pearls, eyeing Barna carefully. The man was slumped in his seat, hands clasped to his face where the boom had struck him. Gloopy looked across the widening gap between the boat and the Cormorant. Dare he risk swimming? Then it happened. With a sizzling flash, lightning struck the boat and Gloopy was hurled into the water with violent force.

8 — The chums in the Cormorant held their breath. The sailboat was a wreck for the lightning had split it like the blow of a huge axe. There was no sign of Barna or Gloopy. Then suddenly the little clown came to the surface gasping for air — with the pearl bag still clutched in his right hand. Immediately Samson dived off the Cormorant, seeing out of the corner of his eye the dark shape of a shark gliding towards the clown.

9 — Two powerful strokes took the strong-man right up to Gloopy and he whirled the little chap clear of the shark's charge. Then Samson turned, streaked back to the Cormorant and heaved Gloopy up on the deck, himself following a moment later. The chums stared out over the water. Other sharks had appeared and they cruised ominously around the wreckage of the sailboat. There was no doubt of Barna's fate. The sharks had got him.

10 — Samson turned grimly away from the water. "There's nothing we can do, chums," he said quietly. "Let's get back to Coral Island. I want to see old Jim's face when he gets his pearls." By skilful sailing Samson took the schooner back through the storm towards the island and when they dropped anchor in the bay, the worst of the storm had passed. Jim Silver, weak from the fever, was there on the beach to meet them, and he could hardly believe his eyes when the grinning Samson poured the pearls into his cupped hands. Jim stammered his thanks.

11 — "There's another present for you, Jim," chuckled Samson, waving a hand at the Cormorant. "You can sail home whenever you like." So a few days later, Jim stepped aboard the boat manned by a dozen islanders. "You circus folks not coming with us?" asked Jim. "No thanks," chuckled Samson. "We like it here!"

Adventures FROM THE GOLDEN YEARS

Samson the Strongman isn't the only hero to have faced a beastly adversary. During their long and colourful history many of **Dandy** and **Beano's** adventurers have found themselves . . .

AT THE MERCY OF MONSTERS!

The WEIRD And WONDERFUL WEST
Part 1

One of the most appealing things about **Dandy** is its unique way of looking at the world, and the comic's version of the Wild West is no exception. **Dandy's** most famous son, **Desperate Dan** — the Texas tough guy with the hard chin and soft heart — has worn a six-gun for over fifty years, but the weapon has rarely left its holster.

Another **Dandy** hero, **Crackaway Jack,** went one better. He didn't pack a pistol, relying instead on a lumberjack's axe, one that was strong enough to fell a full-grown tree and sharp enough to tackle the most bloodthirsty Indian brave.

The **Crackaway Jack** adventure overleaf first appeared in the 1957 **Dandy Book.**

IN the pioneer days in the Wild West, when waggon trains rumbled over the prairie to the golden lands of California, thousands of settlers owed their lives to those fearless plainsmen who blazed the trails and fought off Indian attacks. Greatest of them all was Crackaway Jack, whose amazing exploit — the stealing of the Sacred Eagle Totem Pole of the Arapaho tribe — had made him famous. The great Totem Pole was now held in Fort Resolution as a hostage for the good behaviour of the Arapahoes.

2 — For many moons the Arapahoes had been sullen and quiet. Their war parties raided the Western trails no more. But this was only the calm before the storm, for one day a prairie waggon came hurtling towards the fort pursued by shrieking Indians. The garrison opened the gates for the waggon, then slammed them shut.

3 — "To your posts, men!" ordered Major Butler. The stockade was hurriedly manned. Guns pointed out at the attackers. A few troopers turned to the waggon, and they were the first to die — for that hooded cart was crammed full of Arapahoes! Their trick had got them into the fort, and now they took their terrible toll.

4 — Many of the defenders were taken so much by surprise that they were shot down by arrows in the back. The Redskins hacked with knife and tomahawk at the hated Palefaces. The gates were flung wide. Dozens more of the killers swarmed inside. Fort Resolution fell, fighting to the last. The Indians swarmed over the fort, searching for Crackaway Jack, the Paleface they hated above all others — but they searched in vain. They gathered round their Totem Pole, the real object of the raid, and dug it up.

5 — Crackaway Jack was miles away in the hunting grounds when the raid took place. When he returned to the fort he was greeted by a low moan from a wounded man lying in a scene of dreadful carnage. Only this one man remained alive. "Arapahoes!" he gasped. "Tricked us. Headin' west with the Totem Pole."

6 — Crackaway Jack did what he could for the man, then left the fort at a gallop. Half a mile along the Western trail a message greeted him — a message in red chalk on a big boulder. It was from the masked mystery boy who had helped Crackaway Jack out of many a tight corner before; the boy known as Red Mask.

7 — "Yellow Horse Bluff," mused Jack as he rode. "That's about a mile below the fork of the Muskogee River. I guess Red Mask must have something planned." He was right about Red Mask, for even then the mystery boy was busy. Using a long pole as a lever, he was tumbling rocks down into the right-hand fork of the Muskogee. At this point the channel was deep and narrow, and great masses of shale loosened by the falling rocks soon blocked it. A mighty volume of water was forced into the river's left fork.

8 — Swollen to twice its normal size, the river flowed through a gorge before it passed a spit of land between the fork and Yellow Horse Bluff — and on that flat space, as Red Mask well knew, the Arapahoes were camped, celebrating their recapture of the Sacred Totem Pole. A terrific wall of water suddenly burst out of the bottleneck gorge and swept through the Indian camp like a tidal wave. Nothing could stand in its path, and the braves had no warning of its coming. They were swept away like straws in a gale.

9 — They ran, only to be engulfed. They swam desperately. One valiant brave threw himself astride the Totem Pole as it was wrenched away by the flood, but as he rounded Yellow Horse Bluff on the crest of the wave, a tall figure swung down from a tree and kicked him clean off his perch. Crackaway Jack had not waited in vain.

10 — He had to cling on for all his worth as the Totem was whirled along in the roaring flood. Far behind Crackaway Jack, on a hilltop above the swamped Indian camp, puffs of signal smoke rose high in the air — and the message they conveyed was read by more Arapaho braves paddling up the Muskogee in canoes.

11 — This was the rearguard of the storming party that had raided Fort Resolution. Below a low waterfall they waited for their Totem to fall into their hands. Quietly they waited — and then came the mammoth tidal wave! A pounding, thundering, roaring mass of foaming water, bearing with it the Sacred Totem Pole and its Paleface rider. Crackaway Jack had scooped a long branch from the river. He held it poised like a lance as the Totem Pole plunged down the cataract. Crash! The Totem Pole pounded down on top of a crowded canoe and smashed it to matchwood. The wooden lance thrust red bodies aside like reeds. Tons of swirling water cascaded over the fall and swamped the canoes hurling the warriors to their doom. And Red Mask arrived in time to play a part by hurling rocks into the canoes from the riverbank.

12 — One brave stabbed at Crackaway Jack with a paddle as the Totem Pole surged upwards after its terrific plunge, but the plainsman wrenched it from his grip. From the other side came another Arapaho. He clung to the Totem Pole, striving to knife the Paleface. Crack! A vicious left hook from Crackaway Jack knocked him senseless. Two more warriors flung themselves at the Totem, lunging at the Paleface. A sweep of the paddle hurled them back into the flood, and the great battle was over.

13 — Crackaway Jack finally landed at Salt Flats, where he met Colonel Drever's troop of cavalry on their way to Fort Resolution. The daring plainsman was escorted back to the fort with the Eagle Totem, and there it was erected again, this time in a bed of concrete. With only the aid of Red Mask, Crackaway Jack had defied the whole Arapaho tribe. Without their Totem to safeguard them in war, they would not dare any scalping raids upon the settlers, and the Western trails were safe once more.

The FLIGHT From THE ROARING RIPP

A rip-roaring adventure featuring **Black Bob,** the **Dandy** wonder dog.

"WELL, Bob, I think the sheep will be safe enough for the night, and I know I'll be mighty glad to get my boots off!" sighed Andrew Glenn as he closed the gate and shut the sheep in the fold.

Black Bob wagged his tail. He, too, was weary. They had left the farm near Selkirk early that morning, and had been driving these sheep ever since, for they had to deliver them to their new owner, a farmer down by the coast. The journey was too long to be completed in one day, so they had arranged to stay the night at the little fishing village of Rippton, and Farmer Cockburn had kindly allowed them to pen the flock here for the night.

"Yes, now for the inn and a good meal!" murmured Glenn.

Bob looked up at his master with his big brown eyes, and seemed to understand every word he said.

They started to cross the meadow towards the lane which led to the village. Rippton was a very old fishing port, and sprawled along the left bank of the river Ripp, at the mouth of a valley.

A rumble of thunder made Andrew Glenn turn. He eyed the black clouds hanging over the hills.

"There's a big storm up there, Bob! We got clear of the hills just in time. We were lucky in not having any rain." He studied the direction of the wind. "I don't think the storm will come this way either."

The inn-keeper and his wife were at their door when the shepherd and his collie arrived. Glenn had already arranged for a room. Mrs Milne hurried off to prepare the evening meal.

Again the thunder rolled around the hills up the valley, and lightning zig-zagged in the sky. The inn-keeper frowned.

"There's plenty rain up there by the look of it," he observed. "We've had enough already. The river's swollen as it is."

Andrew Glenn glanced at the broad stream which he could see from the inn window. The waters were brown and ugly, but he saw no cause for alarm, yet.

Ten minutes later both Bob and he were enjoying an excellent meal. It was good to be able to relax, and to know

they would not have to be on the move until seven o'clock in the morning.

Through the window Glenn could see the storm clouds over the hills. They were settling lower.

"I'm glad we didn't delay another day, Bob," he murmured. "It looks as though it may rain all day up there tomorrow. Funny how the hills trap the rain and the coast often misses it!"

Black Bob crunched his teeth on a bone, which he was careful to keep on the newspaper which had been spread on the floor. He was always very careful when he was in other people's homes.

Suddenly the phone on the wall just inside the door rang.

"D'you mind answering that for me, Mr Glenn?" called Mr Milne from the kitchen. "I'm busy at the moment."

"Is that the Rippton Inn?" came the inquiry from the other end. It sounded to Andrew Glenn as though the speaker was breathless.

"It is!" he replied.

"Then, listen carefully! There's been a landslide up here and all the rubble landed in the river. When this blockage breaks there's going to be something like a tidal wave let loose. Tell everyone to get on to high ground. I tried to ring the police station but got no reply . . . Raise the alarm, man! The flood-water might hit you at any moment."

The receiver was slammed down before Glenn could ask who was speaking. Next moment the inn-keeper was at his elbow, asking him what was wrong, for he could tell by the shepherd's face that the news was bad.

"The river's in flood . . . everyone must get on to high ground!" repeated Andrew Glenn.

"I'll warn anyone I can but I've got to see to my sheep. They're too near the river for comfort!"

He began to run up the road with Bob at his heels, and as they went the inn-keeper phoned the police station to find the sergeant had returned. So the news was spread.

Andrew Glenn and Bob had to go about a quarter of a mile to reach the sheep in the fold, and on their way they passed quite a number of houses. As they passed by, Glenn bellowed at the top of his voice. Men and women looked out and gaped

at the running shepherd.

"Get out of your homes and on to high ground!" yelled Glenn. "The river's in flood! Get out as quickly as you can!"

Soon a crowd of men, women and children were streaming up the street behind Glenn and Bob, carrying their belongings. Some pushed hand-carts and prams, piled high with the bedding and valuables they'd managed to grab before dashing outside.

Glenn and Bob got there just in time. Already the water was licking the top of the river bank, not a dozen yards from the sheep.

Within two minutes Bob had cleared the pen, driving the sheep out through the gate, where Glenn was waiting with his crook to prevent them panicking up the valley. He had already selected the spot where he wished to take them, high up the side of the valley beyond the road. He pointed this out to Black Bob, and the dog set to work with a will, urging the terrified animals by every means he knew to go in the right direction. Every now and then a sheep would break away, and Bob would go after it with a tremendous burst of speed and bring it back.

With a final breathless rush Bob and his master drove the flock up the side of the valley to the little meadow which Glenn had seen from below. There they would be safe, and the shepherd turned to see what was happening below.

From there he could see well up the valley, which was no more than a mile wide. It was now filled with leaping, foaming water, and something like a tidal wave was rushing towards the sea, sweeping all before it. Trees, bushes, wooden huts, all were being carried along on the flood.

Presently Bob and Glenn came to where some women and children were huddled on high ground. Some had managed to snatch up a few of their most cherished possessions before being obliged to flee from their homes. They said that the men-folk were out in their boats, trying to rescue those who had been marooned. Not everyone had got away in time, and now there was eight feet of water in the main street. There were sick people who had been left behind, and some aged couples. All possible aid was needed.

Anxious to do his bit, Andrew Glenn ran down the slope towards the flooded village, Black Bob at his heels. Glenn saw a boat between two houses and he shouted to ask if help was needed.

"If ye can pull an oar, yes!" was the prompt reply, and two men came alongside in a heavy boat, which they were scarcely able to hold against the current.

"Where are you making for?" said Glenn, scrambling in with Black Bob.

"Mat Corder's cottage," said Ned, the younger of the fishermen, pointing towards the far side of the village. "He's stranded on the roof of his cottage. We've got to be quick if we're to save him. The water's still rising."

They pulled as though their lives depended on it, but it was hard, heart-breaking work, for the current beat against them savagely. Without the help of Glenn the two fishermen would never have won through. At last they were close enough to shout encouragement to the old man.

The river was racing past on both sides of the cottage, and the walls were cracking under the strain. Already part of the roof had fallen in.

"We daren't go any closer!" panted Sam, the other fisherman.

"Well, do you have a rope?" demanded Glenn.

"Under the seat," said Ned. "But you can't swim through that."

"No," said Glenn grimly. "But Bob can."

He picked up the rope and put one end in Bob's mouth.

"Matthew Corder!" he shouted. "My dog is bringing you the end of a rope. Make it fast round your middle and we'll pull you over."

Then Glenn pointed to the cottage.

"Go on, Bob," he said. "See what you can do."

After a long struggle, Bob got close enough for the marooned man to reach down and grasp the rope.

Three minutes later, exhausted but safe, Corder lay in the bottom of the boat, and Glenn lifted Black Bob aboard.

As they turned to take Corder to a place where he could dry himself and receive attention, there was a crash as his cottage finally collapsed, and a great wave swept past the boat. The old man had been rescued only just in time.

As soon as Mat Corder was safely ashore, the men turned the boat and set out to see if there was anyone else they could help.

Then, suddenly, Ned stood up and grabbed one of the fishermen by the shoulder. "I've just remembered about Bruce!"

"Bruce?" asked Glenn. "Who's he?"

"My father's cart-horse," explained Ned. "My father is a coalman. He keeps the horse in a stable near the station.

"But he's not at home. He was going fishing tonight with some friends. He said he wouldn't be home till midnight."

"We'd better go," suggested Glenn.

The fishermen nodded, and began to row towards the coal merchant's yard. As the boat surged through the gates, Bob suddenly leaped into the bows, whining excitedly. He had heard the frightened neighing of the horse.

"The horse is inside all right," said Glenn grimly. "And no wonder it's in a panic. There must be three feet of water here, and it's rising every minute."

A moment later they arrived at the stable door. As Glenn leaned over to try to open it, he suddenly frowned.

"Confound it! The door's locked," he muttered.

"We'd better get an axe or a crowbar and break the door open," said Sam.

"Haven't you any tools in the boat?" demanded Glenn.

But there was nothing in the boat with which to break open the doors and the fishermen began to row towards the gate.

"Wait!" shouted Glenn. "There's a skylight open on the roof. Bob could get in there. He could be trying to set the horse free while we're looking for an axe."

"Better him than me," said Ned. "I wouldn't fancy going near that horse. Sounds as if it's trying to kick the place to bits. But it's your dog, Mister, if you want to risk it."

So Glenn picked Bob up and pointed to the skylight.
"Go on, boy," he coaxed. "Help Bruce."

Then he threw Bob upwards towards the roof. Bob landed safely and at once scrambled up to the skylight. Bob looked down. There was the horse, frantically rearing up and plunging as it tried to break free from the rope tethering it to the manger.

There was a drop of nearly ten feet facing Bob, but he didn't hesitate. He realised the water below was deep enough to break his fall. He wriggled through the opening and dived into the water. The splash he made scared the horse even more. With a frightened neigh it swung away, stretching the rope to its fullest extent.

That gave Bob his chance. The horse had backed halfway out of the stall. There was enough room for Bob to get past it.

Quickly Bob swam into the stall and climbed on to the manger. Then he seized the halter rope in his teeth and started to chew through it.

The collie kept at it. First one strand and then another parted under his strong, white teeth. Now he had chewed halfway through the rope. That was enough. The constant tugging and straining of the fear-crazed horse did the rest. The rope parted with a crack.

Its back to the door, the huge beast lashed out with its hind legs. That one mighty kick splintered the door from top to bottom, and next second Bruce was outside. Bob followed and saw his master and the fishermen rowing back into the yard.

Glenn had a big axe, but he dropped it and made a grab for the trailing rope as Bruce splashed past.

Then with Bruce wading and sometimes swimming, the fishermen rowed to dry land.

"It's a lucky thing for Rippton that you arrived this evening with your dog, Mister," muttered one of the villagers to Glenn when they all got out of the boat.

By now more than half of the village was under water, but it seemed certain that every human being had been accounted for. The tired rescuers were resting, when there was the sound of a car coming down the steep hill from the north.

Somebody leaped to his feet, exclaiming:

"That's the Commander! We'd forgotten about him. He's been to Edinburgh for the day, as he does every month. Now he'll be in a hurry to get back. He'll drive into the flooded main street if we don't stop him!"

The speaker rushed out into the road and waved his arms at the oncoming car.

It stopped with a screeching of brakes, and a red-faced man put out his head. There was no need to hear his quarter-deck voice to know that he was an old salt. His white beard jutted out stiffly, and his hat was set at a jaunty angle.

"Why are you stopping me, McPherson? Why are all these people gaping at me? What's going on in there — a bun-fight?"

"Sorry, Commander, but you can't go on!" said McPherson. "There's a flood. the main street's under more than ten feet of water. If you go beyond the corner you'll need a submarine instead of a car. That storm in the hills has nearly washed Rippton off the face of the map."

Commander Cruickshank got out and hobbled down to the corner. Andrew Glenn saw that he had a wooden leg. A yell of dismay came from the old man when he saw that only the upper floors of the buildings in the main street showed above the flood, and that the roaring Ripp completely filled the valley. "Blister my timbers, but this is terrrible! What have you done with my pets?"

Andrew Glenn saw everyone look at one another in dismay. In the general excitement they had forgotten all about the Commander's pets.

"He's got two monkeys, three parrots, half a dozen tropical birds, and goodness knows what else. It'll break his heart if anything happens to them," said McPherson.

"Launch the lifeboat!" the Commander was shouting. "My family is in danger. If the water rises another foot they'll all be drowned. Get me a boat and I'll go and fetch them myself."

The tired men looked at him sullenly. If a human life had been in danger they would have roused themselves for another effort, but these were only the Commander's pets, pets which had often annoyed the neighbourhood.

Someone touched him on the arm. It was Andrew Glenn. Andrew did not blame the local men for their refusal, but he wondered if there was not a way of helping.

"Excuse me, Commander, but is a window open to the room where your pets are kept?" he asked.

"Yes! In a few minutes water will be pouring through that window, and —"

"Don't worry," said Glenn reassuringly. "Just point out to me the window you mean."

A few minutes later Black Bob was once again swimming strongly against the flood-water which was pouring down the valley and through the village. This time he carried no rope.

His master had gone down to the water's edge with him, with the old, one-legged man, and Andrew Glenn had pointed to a partially open window about a hundred yards away. He had made Bob understand that he must go there and at once Bob had plunged into the water.

It was hard work. All kinds of things were being swept down with the current — bushes, tree-trunks, empty boxes and chairs. Bob was glad to see that a kitchen table had got caught in this way against the wall below the window.

It was a solid table, and it was floating upside down. He was able to climb on to it and from there on to the window-sill.

The window was wide open, so he did not have to raise it. He jumped down on to the floor inside. Already water had begun to seep over the sill. In a short time it would be pouring into the room.

Cries and screeches came from all around him, and he saw that there were a number of cages, and inside these cages all manner of birds and animals. They were screeching at the sight of him.

Black Bob started nosing at the catch of the nearest cage. Finally he saw how it worked, and he pushed it with his paw. After that it was easy, for all the catches were the same, and he went from cage to cage, opening the doors.

To his surprise neither the animals nor the birds would come out. They were too terrified of him.

Quickly Bob went behind the cages and started snarling and growling. The monkeys at once jumped out through the open doors and flew for the window. When they saw the flood-water outside they crouched chattering on the sill. The squirrels soon followed them, but Black Bob had more trouble with the parrots and the other birds. He almost had to knock their cages over before they flew out and tried to escape through the window. But the Commander had very wisely clipped their wings, and they were unable to fly more than a few yards. They settled on the table outside the window.

"Grr-rr-rrr!" growled Bob, rushing at the animals on the window-sill, and they tumbled out on to the table in panic, clinging there.

Black Bob crouched on the window-sill for a moment. Then he jumped over the heads of the animals and birds on the table and landed in the water with a splash.

He butted the end of the table with his head, until it swung away from the wall of the house and went drifting off with the current.

He pushed it first on one side and then on the other, and so guided it to the spot where Commander Cruickshank and Andrew Glenn were waiting.

Some of the villagers who had heard what was happening cheered as Black Bob climbed out and shook himself, but he dodged all the hands which reached to pat him, and ran to his master.

There was no doubt that the Commander was grateful. He made a great fuss of Bob and gave him some lumps of sugar, too, but eventually Bob slipped away and joined the crowd at the water's edge. The villagers were wondering how long it would be before the flood went down and they could go back to their homes.

Then Bob heard the frightened yelping of a puppy.

He ran down to the edge of the flood-water and stared into the gathering darkness.

Suddenly he traced the noise. A box was floating by, heading for the open sea as the tide ebbed. Clinging to it, whimpering and whining, was a little white puppy. Unless something was done to stop its voyage it would be swept out to sea.

Black Bob raced along the bank and jumped on to a wall. At breakneck speed he dashed along the top of the rough stone-work. It was a foolhardy thing to do. The wall was far from level and some of the stones were loose. One false step and Bob would crash to the ground. But Bob knew the risk had to be taken. If the pup was swept past the end of the wall nothing could save it.

Bob plunged recklessly down the last few yards and splashed into the water. With his paws threshing furiously he struck out for the pup. He reached the box and swiftly grabbed the pup by the loose skin on the back of its neck.

The pup squealed but it had the sense not to struggle. Holding it clear of the water, Bob struggled to the shore. The brave collie did not leave it there, however. He carried it up to the feet of Commander Cruickshank. He knew that the kind-hearted old salt would look after it.

After that Black Bob curled up in a warm corner and went to sleep with his head on his forepaws. He felt that he had done his bit for the night . . .

Andrew Glenn was unable to stay the next day to help with the clearing up after the flood, which subsided as swiftly as it had risen. Bob and he had to deliver the sheep to the new owner twenty miles down the coast.

"One thing's certain," said the inn-keeper, "nobody around here will ever forget your dog. Everyone in the village has learned what you and he did."

Sure enough, when Glenn and Bob left the inn, dozens of folk crowded round to shake the shepherd's hand and to pat the collie's head.

Slowly Bob and his master climbed up the hill with the thanks of the grateful villagers ringing in their ears. At that moment Andrew Glenn felt very proud of his faithful collie.

A BARREL OF LAUGHS!

That was the verdict of **Beano's** readers on the hilarious adventures of **Bucktooth, The Boy Who Lives In A Barrel.**

Despite carrying his house around with him, there was nothing sluggish about **Bucktooth.**

He reckoned it was a great way to travel, rolling along with no mortgage to pay and your only worry, finding a quiet place to park for a spot of shut-eye.

Unfortunately, when **Bucktooth** curled up inside his barrel, things could go wrong. See for yourself in these scenes, and in the story opposite from 4th August 1951.

Bucktooth

THE BOY WHO LIVES IN A BARREL

1 — Complete with a fierce Indian head-dress he had picked up half-price, Bucktooth rolled his barrel far into the bad-lands of the Wild West. The barrel-rolling orphan was heading for Injun Country where the Redskins were still boss and arrows and tomahawks were as common as daisies on a lawn. But Buck wasn't worried! If he met any Redmen he meant to disguise himself as one of them. Besides, he had a lot of other tricks up his sleeve — or, rather, in his barrel. He was sure he could easily fool the Redskins. He had learned a lot in his travels.

2 — There wasn't a Redskin in sight when Buck decided he needed an afternoon nap. But, just as he curled up cosily in a blanket, he heard a clatter of hoofs and a mounted Redskin charged up in full war-paint. The warrior fitted a fire-arrow to his bow and let fly. Wow! The first hint of danger Buck got was a tongue of smoke and flame licking round the side of his barrel. The arrow had landed in the ground beside the barrel and set Buck's rolling home alight. The warrior gave a whoop of triumph. "Paleface in heap big trouble now," he muttered.

3 — The Redskin rode off towards the far horizon while Buck shot from his barrel. "Fire!" he gasped, but there were no fire alarms to ring on the wide, wide prairie. Buck had to be his own fireman and if he hadn't been quick his queer home would have been a lump of charred wood in no time. Seizing the blanket, Buck beat furiously at the flames until he had them under control. Then he mopped his sooty brow and started to clean up the barrel.

4 — Although Buck didn't know, he had sent puffs of smoke drifting into the air and a party of Redskins on a nearby peak saw them. "Look!" exclaimed one, thinking it was a smoke signal. "Somebody say come quick. Beatum drum and tell big chief he wanted straightaway." Tum-tum-tiddley-tum! The drums began to beat. By pure chance Bucktooth had sent a Redskin smoke-signal SOS into the sky.

5 — The SOS was soon answered. Redskins poured from the hills to join the main party and they all rode pell-mell for Buck's camping site. The first hint Buck got that he had used the prairie telegraph was the sight of a horde of Redskins heading for his barrel. But he still wasn't scared. Grinning, he grabbed the Redskin togs from his barrel. "This is where I do my Big Chief Bucktooth act," he muttered. "I'll fool 'em!"

6 — When the Redskins saw Buck dressed up in his finery and wearing the poshest head-dress in the West, they thought he was a big white chief. "Wah!" said their chief. "Paleface with wooden wig-wam wears buffalo head. Him heap powerful. We must smokum pipe of peace with him." He squatted down sternly and thrust the peace-pipe towards Buck while his warriors crowded round. But Buck had HIS smoking equipment ready.

7 — Yes, sir! Buck was no fool. He didn't mean to poison his insides with a smelly old peace-pipe just to make friends with the Indians and save his scalp. But he had another plan. "Me smokum special peace-pipe," he said to the chief. "Heap magic tobacco." Craftily Buck mixed some soapy water, then he stuck his clay-pipe in his mouth and began to blow bubbles like the expert he was. Big bubbles and small sailed from the pipe.

8 — The Redskin chief was pop-eyed when he saw the odd smoke coming from Buck's clay-pipe. "Um! Truly this is special peace medicine," he grunted. Then he said, "Me next!" in Redskin talk and grabbed the pipe from Buck. Poor Chief Whopping Nose! He did only one thing wrong. He sucked instead of blowing. He foamed at the mouth, but he passed the pipe on, determined that all his followers should try it.

9 — Buck had really meant to show the Redskins how to blow bubbles and put them in a good mood that way, but now it seemed too late to start. All the Redmen from Big Chief Whopping Nose down to Little Sitting Bull were groaning and clutching their stomachs. All of them were blowing bubbles, too, but blowing bubbles from your mouth isn't good fun like blowing them from a clay-pipe! They all looked a nice shade of green beneath their war-paint. "White Chief sell bad medicine," groaned Whopping Nose. "Him die pronto!" But Buck had already hopped into his barrel and was legging it back the way he had come. He knew it was no good trying to explain to the Indians. The Redskins were too sick to chase him but they all had tomahawks, spears and arrows handy. Buck knew that. That was why he was using his barrel as an armoured suit.

10 — Zoom! Whoosh! Thud! The Redskins had sore tummies and every time they moved, their heads began to swim. But they hadn't lost their skill with their weapons. First a tomahawk, then an arrow, then a spear hit the barrel — then a shower of each. Buck kept on running, trying his best to keep his skin clear of the sharp points sticking through the barrel. The thought of the armoury he was carrying made him run faster. He didn't want his foes to get their weapons back and have another try.

11 — When the Indians had fired every arrow and hurled every tomahawk and spear they lay down and groaned. Soon Buck left the tribe of mighty sick Redmen far behind and was well out of Injun Country, determined not to return for many a day. But when he finally got out of the barrel in a little Western town he realised his journey hadn't been for nothing. In no time Buck was doing a roaring trade selling souvenir spears, arrows and tomahawks to tourists arriving by stagecoach.

From a barrel of laughs to a bundle of fun — **Barney's Bear.** This story, featuring one of **Dandy's** cuddliest characters, first appeared in the 1956 Annual.

BARNEY'S BEAR

SMARTY was a jolly little black bear cub who was the special pet of Barney Brennan and Digger Merry, the gold-mining partners. They were camping in the Canadian backwoods, and everything was merry and bright but for one little thing. That little thing was the cheeky, sneaky Snowy, the white bear cub who had also become a pet in the camp. The two wee bears were great rivals, and were forever playing tricks on each other. Right at this moment, Smarty had thought of a great joke to play on Snowy.

2 — He had caught a frog, and he put it inside a meat pie, which he made sure went on Snowy's plate at dinner-time. It was very funny to see the amazement in the white cub's face when that pie got up and ran away! The frog had forced its strong hindlegs through the bottom, and it went flipping away, hop, hop, hop for all its worth.

3 — Snowy was too greedy to let a meat pie escape him, even though there was something alive inside it. He rose and chased the leaping pie as it bounded over the grass towards Bear Creek Gorge. The frog didn't see where it was going, and it was only by sheer luck that it flipped along a tree trunk spanning the gorge.

4 — Growling with rage, Snowy ran along the trunk after his pie. And it was because his eyes were on the pie that he failed to see a greasy-looking patch on the tree. When he planted a paw on that greasy patch he skidded, slipped sideways, and tumbled headlong from the log — right into the mesh of a net that hung below!

5 — The net closed up, and Snowy swung with a thump against the wall of the gorge. When he got his breath back he found himself a prisoner, dangling in a string bag. Smarty hugged himself with glee when he saw Snowy. But he couldn't leave him there. Barney would be angry. So he got hold of a knife and ripped open Snowy's prison.

6 — Snowy didn't feel at all grateful to Smarty for saving him from the net. That trap had been set by three strange men, and when Snowy saw them at work a little later in the woods he began to wonder if the strange job they were doing might help him to get rid of Smarty. For the white cub was wise enough to know that it was a spring trap the men were rigging up. Holding his breath to avoid being discovered, crafty Snowy waited till the trap was baited with a jar of honey. After the men had gone the clearing was quiet.

7 — It was a bear the trappers were after. Snowy guessed that, and his little eyes gleamed as he decided to help them to get one. Smarty was on the prowl not far away. He was moving from bush to bush looking for berries, and when he drew near, Snowy leapt out into the open and threw a stone at his rival to attract his attention.

8 — Turning with a fierce growl, Smarty chased after Snowy to get his own back. But suddenly in his path he saw the jar of honey sitting on a mound of grass and twigs. And, of course, being a hungry little cub and very fond of honey, he postponed his revenge for a few seconds while he paused to snatch up the jar. As he did so — Crash!

9 — Smarty's weight on the concealed board released the spring that held the cage trap down. At once the cage came flying up from under its screen of grass, up and over and down with a crash that made the wee cub jump. Barney's Bear groaned when he realised he was trapped. There were bars all around him, and he couldn't move them, no matter how he tried. He heard nothing but gurgles of glee from the bush where Snowy crouched. Then came footsteps. "We've got something," a man cried. "Yes, it's a bear cub!"

10 — There were three of the men altogether, all of them ugly customers, and they carried Smarty away to a clearing and put him in another cage made of rough logs. All around him, he noticed, were other caged animals, among them a bear, a lynx and a cougar. One was uncaged. It was a great big moose tethered to a tree.

11 — When the men had gone into their tent Smarty used the brains behind those sparkling little eyes of his! Making a friendly growl in his throat, Barney's Bear attracted the moose towards him. The huge animal was curious. It came nuzzling over to Smarty's cage — and Smarty suddenly biffed it on the big snout!

12 — That did it! The moose recoiled and its eyes sparked fire. With an angry snort it lowered its enormous spread of horns and charged at Smarty. Its tether rope broke under the strain, and then the whole thundering weight of the moose crashed against Smarty's cage. What a smash-up. Logs cracked and splintered and flew through the air, and Smarty, crouching in a corner out of harm's way, was quick to seize his chance of freedom, while the moose, dazed by the collision, sprawled amongst the ruins.

13 — But now the trappers were aroused. Their heads appeared at the tent door, and Smarty realised in a flash what he must do if he wanted to escape. Quick as a wink he raced from cage to cage, unfastening the doors to release the imprisoned animals, and the air was filled with the howls and snarls of the wild beasts as they sighted the men who had trapped them. With cries of alarm, these men took to their heels as soon as the first cage was opened. Next moment the lynx, the cougar and the rest were after them.

14 — The three men had to take refuge up a tree, and when Smarty saw this he made a bee-line for Barney's camp. There was a newcomer with his men pals, and when they heard the hubbub in the distance they all went to see what was causing it. This newcomer was a game warden, and trapping animals wasn't allowed in his forest.

15 — The three crooked trappers went to jail. All the animals regained their freedom. But Smarty came best of all out of the adventure, for the game warden insisted on giving Barney's Bear the feast of a lifetime for the good work he had done. Barney and Digger shared in it, but crafty Snowy was left shivering out in the cold.

'YOU AND WHOSE ARMY?'

That wasn't something playground bullies said to young Alfie Johnson, because he did have his own army. Alfie, better known to **Beano** readers as **General Jumbo,** had a force of tiny troops at his command.

Invented by Jumbo's friend Professor Carter, and controlled by a gadget strapped to the youngster's wrist, the model army proved a huge hit with readers in the 1950s — a time when collecting toy soldiers was a popular schoolboy hobby.

The stories overleaf first appeared in October 1953.

Adventures GENERAL JUMBO

1 — "The Army exercises are about to begin!" chuckled young Jumbo Johnson, as he stood proudly in Dinchester Park. "Very good, General Jumbo, sir," returned the plump, cheery-faced man beside Jumbo, and he began to strap a strange gadget to Jumbo's left arm. The man was Professor Carter, Jumbo's greatest friend, and that gadget was the wonderful device by which Jumbo controlled an Army by radio. All his soldiers, tanks and planes were small, perfectly-made models. They were all stowed neatly away in the Professor's van which was parked nearby.

2 — The models were the marvellous invention of the Professor, and as a reward for saving the Professor's life, the brilliant inventor had put Jumbo in charge of his models. Now Jumbo was going to have full-scale manoeuvres in the park. As the Prof. went off to open his van, Jumbo heard a boy's startled shout. The sound was coming from the other side of a hedge and quickly Jumbo ran to see what the trouble was. Some children were having a picnic — and a scruffy individual was trying to steal their food, which they had brought in a hamper.

3 — "Clear off, you kids," growled the man, giving one of the boys a push that sent him rolling on the ground. "I'll have that grub." Jumbo's eyes glinted. "This is a job for the Army," he muttered, and ran over to the van, the back of which the professor was busy opening. Quickly Jumbo told the Professor about the thieving lout and the two friends held a quick council-of-war to decide how best to make their attack.

4 — From the other side of the hedge came the sound of another blow and a yell of pain. Jumbo gave a quick glance into the open back of the van. On the shelves inside were rows and rows of small, model soldiers, tanks, vehicles and planes. Jumbo began to twiddle the knobs and buttons on the control gadget, and immediately tanks and soldiers started to move down ramps leading out of the van. "Prepare for action!" called General Jumbo.

5 — Left-right! Left-right! The tiny soldiers marched in step and the tanks rumbled along in a long column. Jumbo, busy with the controls, took his models to the end of the hedge and halted them. He peered round. The children were huddled beside the hedge, and now the thief had the picnic to himself. Jumbo pressed two buttons on the controls. Two of the tanks began to roll forward and two soldiers charged with fixed bayonets.

6 — The scruffy thief was licking his lips as he cut himself a thick slice of bread. "I'll have a nice, juicy, jam sandwich to start with," he muttered. "Then half a dozen o' them tarts, then — OW!" The lout leaped to his feet with a startled yelp of pain. Jumbo's leading soldier had jabbed the ruffian in the seat of his ragged trousers. "OW!" He yelled again as the second soldier's bayonet pierced his leg.

7 — The thief whipped round and saw his midget attackers. He just gaped. Then the two soldiers charged again. With a frightened howl the ruffian began to run. But Jumbo was ready for that. He had brought the two tanks round to cut off the tramp's escape. Now the boy brought the whole squadron into action. The tiny turret guns swivelled round and — pop! pop! pop! — volleys of hard peas peppered the lout's face.

8 — The startled rascal jumped about six feet in the air, and his legs fairly twinkled as he scuttled off across the park! But Jumbo wasn't finished with the crook. He had launched a flight of his miniature jet fighters, and now they went screaming towards their target. The rascal was pelting along past the children's paddling pool when the planes overtook him, and their lightning swoops drove him into the water.

9 — Wheeeee! The high-pitched whining of the jets drowned the ruffian's yells of fear. With arms flailing like windmill sails, he tried to smash the annoying planes. But Jumbo's skill at the controls prevented the jets from being hit. Wet from head to foot, the tramp hared out of the Park entrance which a workman was busy painting. With a chuckle, Jumbo made one of his planes swoop towards a paint pot. The plane's wing knocked over the pot and bright red paint landed on the thief's head.

10 — Down the street staggered the lout, scuttling about like a frightened hen. And after him went Jumbo and his planes. As he passed the painter, Jumbo apologised for using the paint-pot as a bomb. "Sorry, mister," he yelled. "That rotter's been pinching food." The painter nodded in understanding. But now the ruffian had given up trying to escape. He was clinging desperately to a lamp-post with the planes buzzing briskly round him. They never gave him a moment's peace.

11 — "Call 'em off!" whined the crook, as General Jumbo came up to him, followed by nearly every boy and girl in the neighbourhood. Word had spread quickly about Jumbo's miniature Army going into action against a thief, and scores of children had come to see the fun. Jumbo looked stern. "You are my prisoner!" he said in the gruffest voice he could muster. "On your feet!" The lout shakily obeyed, and gave an extra big shudder as the Professor came up with the tanks and soldiers. Jumbo arranged them on either side of the captive as an escort. "Prisoner and escort — atten-shun!" rapped Jumbo. "To the police-station — quick, MARCH!" Off went the marching column, and soon the rascal was behind bars, while Jumbo and his Army were back in the Park. And the children held their picnic — with General Jumbo as the guest of honour!

Adventures

1 — There was a sea-battle in full swing off the seashore at Dinchester. Nobody was getting hurt — the ships and planes in the battle were models, with young Alfie Johnson directing operations. Alfie, known to his pals as Jumbo, was kneeling on a rock on the beach, grinning all over his face as he watched a small destroyer squirt a jet of water at a swooping seaplane. All the time Jumbo was twiddling the tiny knobs and buttons on a mysterious gadget strapped to his wrist. This was the marvellous "box of tricks" that controlled the models by radio. Young Jumbo was an expert at operating the cleverly-made controls.

2 — The amazing models had been built by Professor Carter, a scientist whose life Jumbo had saved. As a reward, the Prof. had allowed Jumbo to take charge of his models! In addition to ships and planes, Jumbo had tanks, guns, cars and soldiers, all models. He was really in control of a miniature Army, Navy and Air Force. Jumbo made his flying boat glide down upon the water, and suddenly his grin vanished. Several yards off-shore, a rowboat was drifting towards a sinister black object in the water. It was an explosive naval mine which could be set off by contact with the boat. The angler in the boat was fast asleep.

3 — "Hi, there! Look out!" Jumbo's yell of warning drifted out over the water. But the man in the boat did not waken. He must have been in a very deep sleep. And the distance between boat and mine was closing rapidly. Jumbo's right hand shot to the control panel. There was not a moment to lose. With a whine of tiny jet motors, the flying boat surged forward, and in a moment was rising like a seabird from the water.

4 — Now the rowboat was barely three yards from the mine and still the fisherman slept on, unaware of his terrible danger. Jumbo's fingers moved swiftly over the controls and the flying boat wheeled and swooped over the boat. At the same time the rear gun-turret swung round and — swoosh! — a jet of water squirted from the gun and splashed in the angler's face. He awoke with a jerk that made the little boat rock violently.

5 — "Who's that throwing water?" spluttered the man, while Jumbo's urgent voice made him sit up with a start. "Row like mad!" yelled the boy. "A mine!" The man saw the sinister black object now barely a yard from his boat. In half a tick he was at the oars pulling like a galley slave and the boat shot away from the mine. With a gasp of relief Jumbo brought back his flying boat and grabbed it as it came gliding towards him.

6 — But Jumbo's face was still grim. The mine was drifting to Dinchester's busy harbour and beach which were swarming with people. None of them had seen the mine. A quick warning was needed. Swiftly Jumbo took a small cylinder from the funnel of one of his destroyers. It was a little flask containing a smoke-making liquid. Quickly Jumbo opened a panel in the fuselage of the flying boat and began to pour the liquid into a tiny tank.

BEWARE···OF···THE···MINE

7 — Jumbo was too busy to notice the man in the row-boat. The boat had grounded on the shore nearby and the angler scrambled out and flopped breathless on the sand, gasping out his thanks to Jumbo. The boy looked for the mine again. It was much nearer the little harbour. Jumbo launched his seaplane into the sky. Up and up soared the aircraft and the folks on the harbour and the beach looked skywards. They saw the flying boat level out high over the beach and saw smoke begin to stream from it. Jumbo, handling the controls with expert ease, made the plane loop and whirl and as it did so the smoke formed into the letters of a message. Jumbo's plane was sky-writing! Quickly the words took shape — "Beware of the Mine."

8 — A hush settled over the beach and all at once the people saw the deadly drifting mine. Then there was panic as the picnickers and bathers snatched up their belongings and ran up from the beach. Jumbo brought his plane down and mopped his forehead. He had prevented what might have been a terrible disaster on the beach. But the mine was still drifting towards the little ships in the harbour. "There's only one thing for it!" Jumbo muttered, and set one of his destroyers in motion.

9 — Its powerful motor purring smoothly, the little vessel sped out into the bay. With clever movements of the controls, Jumbo brought the destroyer round in a sharp turn to port. Then the boy looked at the harbour. The last man was running along the quay. Now it would be safe for Jumbo to carry out his plan. He touched a button on the control panel. The destroyer leapt forward, heading straight for the mine. The sharp little bows cut the water as the small vessel worked up to full speed.

10 — Closer and closer sped the destroyer and Jumbo, tensed in every muscle, kept the ship on its course. The townsfolk, under cover and free from danger, watched excitedly. Then the destroyer struck the mine and — BOOM! — a thunderous roar rocked the town as the mine exploded and blew the model destroyer to pieces. Young Jumbo gulped. "Bang goes one of the finest little ships in the world," he muttered. "But it was well worth it."

11 — The crowds surged forward and in a moment Jumbo was surrounded. "Well done, lad!" "Great work, Jumbo!" Jumbo just grinned. He had lost one of the Professor's best models, but he had saved many lives and ships. Jumbo was the hero of the town and the very next day the Mayor of Dinchester presented him with a special award for cleverness and skill. General Jumbo had won his first medal!

General Jumbo must have had long-life batteries in his radio-control box, because his adventures kept going strong through the 1960s and into the 1970s, when he was 'promoted' to **Admiral Jumbo!**

OUT OF THIS WORLD!

If you asked Beano fans which of their heroes was 'out of this world', they'd probably answer "All of 'em!" But there was one in particular who could confidently claim that title . . . **Jack Flash,** the boy from Planet Mercury.

With wings at his ankles, Jack could move quick as a flash, and being able to fly came in handy when your Earth pals were broke.

But giving your mates the best view at a cricket match was no big deal for Jack. As you'll see overleaf, a trip with this Beano superstar could take you much farther afield . . .

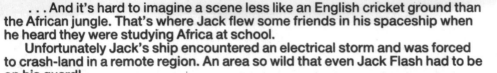

. . . And it's hard to imagine a scene less like an English cricket ground than the African jungle. That's where Jack flew some friends in his spaceship when he heard they were studying Africa at school.

Unfortunately Jack's ship encountered an electrical storm and was forced to crash-land in a remote region. An area so wild that even Jack Flash had to be on his guard!

This exciting story, the conclusion of which appears on the following pages, first entertained Beano readers in 1956.

JA

JACK FLA⚡H

R ELUCTANTLY, Jack Flash and his chums were bidding farewell to their pygmy guides. They were anxious to explore a mysterious cavern which lay hidden behind a mighty waterfall in the wilds of Africa. The pygmies stood in the cave-mouth refusing to go farther. The Flying Boy was sorry to leave the pygmies, for they had befriended him and his schoolboy chums ever since Jack's space ship had crash-landed in the jungle. Now there was a mystery to be solved. An earthquake had split open the bed of the lake near the pygmy village. The waters had drained away, revealing the hulk of an ancient Roman galley on the lake bed.

2 — The lake bed had also yielded another relic — a carved bronze standard bearing the Roman eagle crest. The pygmy Chief had recognised the crest. He had seen it carved on the wall of the mysterious cave. Having led Jack and the boys to the clue in the cave, the chief would go no farther. From now on the boys were on their own! The boys, keen history students, estimated this Roman galley and standard were 2000 years old. Tales of lost Roman legions sprang to mind as they headed through the cave. Suddenly, the tunnel came to a dead end. A wall of rock barred their way, but high up on the wall was another carving of a Roman eagle.

3 — Once more Jack's amazing flying powers came in handy. Watched by his excited chums, he flew up to the carving and hovered in mid-air to study it closely. His eyes took in every detail of the crest. It had been expertly hewn out of the granite-like rock. Curiously Jack stretched out his hand to finger the carving. Who could tell how old it was?

4 — As Jack's hand touched the carving he was surprised and puzzled to hear faint creaking sounds. Gasps of astonishment came from the watching boys below. The lower half of the rock face was opening outwards on strong hinges. By touching the crest, Jack must have operated some strange secret mechanism. The boys stared in awe as the huge rock door swung open.

5 — Excitedly, Jack and his chums ventured through the opening, every muscle in their bodies tensed for action. After this unexpected development, they knew anything might happen. Even so, they were bewildered by what they saw. From the grotto a great flight of steps led down into a broad valley. In the valley nestled a strange city, the like of which they had seen only in history books! The beautiful, columned buildings and arch-ways were those of a lost Roman city.

6 — The boys gaped in silent wonder at the startling panorama. As they saw people moving in the walled city below, they knew that the mystery was solved. They had found a lost Roman civilisation. The city was hidden from the outside world by wild mountains, which enclosed it on all sides: Jack's discovery of the entrance to it had been a chance in a million. The boys broke into excited chatter. It was possible that they were the only outside people to have seen the city since its construction.

7 — "Let's go down, Jack!" urged the boys excitedly. Jack was wary. "Stick close together then!" he said cautiously. He wasn't certain what sort of welcome they would receive from the Romans. He was taking no chances. It was fortunate that Jack was on the alert. No sooner had they left the staircase than a fierce lion bounded from the cover of the rocks. The beast was injured. An arrow was embedded in its tawny hide. It was obviously being hunted, for it kept glancing behind as it ran.

8 — Fortunately, the lion was too concerned with escaping its pursuers to bother about the defenceless boys. They stood rooted to the spot in horror as it bounded across their path. Suddenly there came a pounding of hooves and Jack saw a Roman hunter giving chase in his chariot. He was hot in pursuit of the wounded lion, spear raised for the kill. The boys scattered in the hunter's path, but young Tommy Green stumbled and fell right in front of the charging horse.

9 — The swarthy Roman hunter, bent on a kill, had no eyes for the boy in his path. Swiftly Jack launched himself into flight in a neck-or-nothing attempt to save Tommy from the flashing hooves of the galloping horse. Jack grabbed for the reins of the chariot and jerked on them with all his might. The startled horse reared upwards as the boy pulled its head to one side. The chariot lurched violently and skidded sideways. Thanks to Jack's quick-witted action Tommy had escaped death by inches!

10 — While Jack struggled to rein-in the rearing horse, the boys rushed to the aid of the Roman hunter, who had been thrown from his chariot by the sudden jolt. He lay winded and dazed on the ground, and Tommy Green tried to assist him to his feet. Then, as Jack got the horse under control, a fleet of chariots manned by Roman soldiers came thundering to the scene. The soldiers' faces were grim and menacing as they saw the boys clustered round their fallen comrade.

11 — With swords drawn, the soldiers leapt from their chariots and surrounded the boys. Slowly the winded hunter rose to his knees, a scowl on his face. He wore a black plumed helmet, and looked to be a man of importance, probably a centurion. He gave a sharp order, and Tommy and his pals were seized roughly and their arms pinned behind their backs. A few of the boys tried to make a break for it, but were easily rounded up by the watchful charioteers. Jack Flash hovered above, unable to help.

12 — Recovered from his fall, the Roman leader glared up into the sky, looking for the strange Flying Boy who had caused the incident. He saw Jack hovering by the top of a palm tree, and knew he couldn't hope to catch him — yet! The angry Roman shook his fist threateningly. Jack had realised it was futile to try and free his chums at the moment. He could help them most by avoiding capture. As the boys were herded off into the city by the soldiers, Jack followed above, biding his time.

JACK FLASH hovered anxiously in the cloudless African sky. Below him, in a valley enclosed by wild mountains, nestled a strange, walled city. It was the home of a lost Roman colony, a civilisation which was 2000 years old. The Flying Boy from Mercury and his schoolboy chums were marooned in Africa as the result of a crash landing in Jack's space-ship. They had stumbled on the entrance to this mysterious valley, but the Romans had proved far from friendly and had taken the boys prisoner. Jack, however, had escaped and was now planning their rescue. The boys were to be sold as slaves in the city's market-place.

2 — Dodging in and out of the tall, pillared buildings, Jack swooped down for a closer view of the market-place. A crowd had collected round the platform. Uniformed centurions mingled with the wealthy citizens and merchants in their togas. His chums stood bunched together under the menace of a big fellow wielding a whip. The slave dealer, an old bearded rascal in flowing robes, pushed young Tommy Green roughly to the front. "What am I bid for this strapping lad?" A fierce-looking centurion started the bidding at ten pieces of silver. Slowly the price rose until a wealthy merchant held up a bag of coins worth thirty pieces of silver.

3 — "Sold!" No one raised the fat merchant's bid and the slave dealer promptly accepted it. The rascal rubbed his hands greedily. These young slaves gave promise of fetching fat prices. The merchant, too, was pleased with his purchase. This sturdy lad would serve him well. Young Tommy Green scowled truculently. He had no fears. Jack Flash would not let his pals down. At that very moment, as yet unseen by anyone, Jack was indeed coming to their aid.

4 — The Flying Boy had seen enough. He had bided his time, but when the merchant made to claim his slave, Jack knew the time was ripe for action. As the merchant handed over his bag of coins to the slave dealer, Jack suddenly swooped down from his hiding-place on a nearby rooftop. Thrusting the merchant aside he snatched the bag of coins from his fist. The other buyers drew back in surprise and alarm at sight of this strange boy who could fly like a bird.

5 — The bag of coins was the key to Jack's plan. Swiftly he wheeled and flew over the heads of a mixed crowd of onlookers at the rear of the buyers. These onlookers were the poorer element of the city — labourers, hired hands and beggars. Cunningly, Jack scattered the silver coins in their midst. Immediately, the market place was in an uproar as the rabble scrambled for the coins — a fortune to many of them.

6 — This diversion was just what Jack had hoped for. The soldiers, caught up in the scramble, were powerless as the crowd fought amongst themselves for the silver. Without delay, Jack turned to the task of freeing his chums. In the commotion, only the burly figure with the whip remained to guard them. With a flying charge, Jack heaved the guard off the platform and yelled to the boys to make a break for it. They obeyed swiftly.

7 — As fast as their legs could carry them, the boys raced through the streets, heading for the gateway by which they had entered the city. Jack overpowered two soldiers and seized their shields to cover the boys' retreat. Then he, too, made his escape. At the gateway, a squad of guards threatened to foil the escape. Holding the shields in front of him, Jack became a flying battering-ram and cleared a path through the soldiers.

8 — By now the alarm had been raised and more soldiers came racing to the scene to prevent the boys escaping from the secret city. "This way!" shouted Billy Wilson, spotting an empty chariot by the gateway. One by one the boys followed him and clambered aboard, while Jack remained behind to hold off the attack. The Romans were bewildered by this strange and elusive enemy. They couldn't get to grips with him.

9 — Finally Jack hurled his shields aside and joined his chums. He leapt astride the horses' backs, seized the reins, and urged the animals into a gallop. At a furious pace he drove through the great arched gateway of the walled city and headed out across the valley. In a matter of moments the Romans were mobilised, too, and a fleet of chariots were rattling and bumping in pursuit. Then, with bewildering suddenness, a fierce earth tremor shook the valley. The ground seemed to erupt underneath them.

10 — Jack and the boys chilled in horror. Once before, on the other side of the mountain, they had suffered the terrors of an earthquake. It had followed in the wake of a volcanic eruption. With a crack, the ground behind them split open in a great fissure. The leading pursuers plunged into the yawning chasm. Looking round, the boys saw the Roman city crumble and fall before their very eyes. Shaken to their foundations, building after building crashed in heaps of rubble.

11 — The pursuing Romans were engulfed in falling stones and rubble. Desperately, Jack Flash spurred the terrified horses onwards towards the rocky tunnel by which he and his chums had entered the valley. Pulling the chariot to a halt, he ushered the boys up the great stone stairway to the tunnel entrance. Hastily they glanced over their shoulders for a last look at the valley. It was a scene of havoc. The proud city had been razed to the ground. Not one building remained standing. Clouds of dust rose from the rubble and the city was lost to view.

12 — "Hurry, boys! Hurry!" cried Jack urgently. The earthquake was by no means over. All around them the ground was cracking and crumbling threateningly. Desperately the chums raced under the strange raised trapdoor of rock and bolted into the tunnel. They had no sooner done so than the stone door crashed to the ground and the ceiling of the cavern began to give way. Huge boulders fell around them as they ran. It looked as if they might well share the fate of the lost Roman colony and be wiped out by the earthquake.

A SEAPLANE whizzed out of a cloud in the African sky and flew low over a jungle-fringed lake. Standing by the lakeside were Jack Flash and his chums. They whooped joyfully as the plane winged overhead. They knew it to be a rescue plane searching for them. Jack, who came from the planet Mercury, possessed tiny ankle wings which gave him the flying powers of a bird. With his schoolboy chums from Helmsford High School and their teacher, Mr Moon, Jack had been marooned in the jungle as a result of a crash-landing in his jet spaceship. The teacher, fevered by the sting of a scorpion, had been evacuated by a smaller plane earlier.

2 — Because of the dense jungle background, Jack knew it was unlikely that the pilot had spotted them as he flew over. Hurriedly, with the boys' help, he set about building a fire to attract the pilot's attention. He took care to build it where the lake looked safest for landing. The lake, recently emptied by an earthquake, was rapidly being filled again by the waterfall at its head. The waterfall feeding the lake was formed by the meeting of many streams, in that mountainous area. The boys went to work with a will, thinking of how the tales of their jungle adventures would thrill their pals at home. They got the fire going and waited for the plane to return.

3 — Suddenly, just as the smoke of their bonfire signal began to spiral skywards, the cool breeze which fanned the flames grew stronger in force. Without any warning, the breeze had become a terrifying, swirling fury. The boys were sucked off their feet and sent spinning to the ground by the sheer force of the wind and flying dust. It was a freak whirlwind and its initial fury hit them like the blast of an explosion. Jack guessed it was an after-effect of the recent earthquakes which had hit the area.

4 — With his strange ankle wings whirring powerfully, Jack struggled to stay airborne. For a moment he was blinded by the black smoke of the fire as the wind swept it into his face. Then, as he opened his eyes again, he saw that the heaped faggots of wood forming the bonfire were being scattered in all directions. Like flares, the burning faggots were flying through the air, caught in the grip of the swirling wind. Jack seized a pole and attempted to beat out the small fires which had started.

5 — For the moment, the rescue plane was forgotten. As the boys struggled to stay on their feet, their only thoughts were of the danger of the fire spreading. Try as they might, the boys were fighting a losing battle. The freak fury was too powerful. Then, as suddenly as it had appeared, the whirlwind vanished. The damage was done, however. Jack and his chums could only watch helplessly as the jungle fringe went up in flames.

6 — Soon the whole jungle was ablaze. In the dry, rain-starved undergrowth the flames spread swiftly. Above the crackling of the flames there came more urgent and menacing sounds. The animal life of the jungle was being driven from its home. First, a squawking flock of birds flapped out of the treetops. Then came a strange collection of wild beasts. Desperately Jack and the boys leapt into the lake. Only the water could save them.

7 — The lake was well below its normal level and the boys were able to wade into the centre of it without getting out of their depth. They were closely followed by the strange herd of wild beasts. Elephants, lions and giant hippos mingled with the less fierce zebras, giraffes and deer. Natural enemies were united for the moment in the panic of the stampede. Soon the lake was teeming with swimming animals. All the time Jack hovered over the boys' heads, alert and watchful.

8 — Fortunately, the wild beasts were too intent on saving themselves to molest the defenceless boys. Suddenly there was a roar of engines overhead and the seaplane zoomed out of the pall of smoke which hung over the jungle. The pilot had seen the fire and the activity on the lake and had come down to take a closer look. As the plane zoomed past at treetop level, the boys in the water waved frantically. They sighed with relief as the pilot dipped his wings. He had seen them.

9 — Slowly the plane banked and climbed higher to circle the lake. Jack's brow furrowed thoughtfully. The pilot could not hope to land on the lake while the animals remained. It was too risky. On the other hand, he could only keep circling as long as his fuel supply lasted. Jack made a quick decision. If the plane couldn't come down to them, they would go up to meet it! He could carry the boys up one by one. It was a risk, but he knew that if his strength held out, all would be well.

10 — Quickly Jack outlined his plan to his chums and told Tommy Green to climb on to his back. The boys were not afraid. They had good reason to trust Jack's amazing flying powers. Thrust by his ankle wings, Jack flew up to intercept the plane, with Tommy clinging tightly to his shoulders. The strange human airlift had begun. Up, up they zoomed. The pilot was ready. His navigator opened a side-hatch in the plane's fuselage and Jack was able to stow Tommy safely aboard.

11 — Jack seemed tireless. One by one he ferried his young pals up to the rescue plane. The pilot manoeuvred his plane carefully and skilfully, helping Jack as much as he could. Soon every boy was safe inside the aircraft, and together the chums crowded into the cockpit cabin for a final look at the wild jungle which had been their home for so long. It hardly seemed possible that they had survived its dangers.

12 — A few, thrilling days later, the boys arrived home in Helmsford by air-liner. Their teacher, Mr Moon, now fully recovered from his fever, was the first to greet them at the airport. The boys' parents were there, too, and they joined heartily in the cheers as the boys hoisted Jack shoulder-high. All the boys knew they owed their lives to their amazing pal, the Flying Boy from Mercury.

The WEIRD And WONDERFUL WEST —Part III—

Unless you're reading this book backwards, you'll know about Crackaway Jack, the guy who packed an axe rather than a pistol. And if you thought that was weird — you ain't seen nothin' yet, Pardner! In the 1960 Dandy Book, Wild West fans were treated to a tale where the hero was a wardrobe. Yes . . . A WARDROBE! Other books and comics told how the West was won. Dandy chose to show its readers how the West was FUN!

DIGGER'S WANDERING WARDROBE

CROOKED NOSE and Crazy Horse were Piute Indians, and they had no right to be in Digger Marr's log cabin here in North-West Canada. It was Digger's big wardrobe mirror that fascinated them.

They had never seen a mirror as big as this and they play-acted in front of it.

Digger had been out prospecting, and his feet made no sound in the powdery snow when he returned. He pushed the door open.

YOU THIEVIN' VARMINTS! WHAT ARE YE DOIN' IN MY SHACK?

COME BACK HERE! I'LL PERFORATE THE PAIR O' YE!

But the braves were out through the window like greased lightning. Digger seized his rifle and went injun-hunting, only to walk right into an ambush.

Crazy Horse and Crooked Nose left the prospector lying senseless. They went to his cabin and came out carrying that wonderful wardrobe.

They bore it away over the snows.

And when the prospector did wake up, groaning, he staggered back to his cabin to get the shock of his life. When he turned from bandaging up his head, he missed it right away — his wardrobe — GONE!

MY GOLD, MY FURS, MY SPARE RIFLE — THEY WERE ALL IN THAT WARDROBE. BUT I'LL TRACK IT DOWN IF IT TAKES ME A WEEK.

The trail of the wardrobe-pinchers led to the far-off village of the Piute tribe. Digger got there by sundown and halted to eat — and think. If he entered the village openly, the wardobe would be kept out of sight. He must plan some kind of trick.

NOW THAT NEW-FANGLED PLASTIC BAG FOR HOLDING GRUB GIVES ME A REAL GOOD NOTION.

Digger hurried off to a place he had found while prospecting — a place where natural gas hissed from holes in the ground. Squatting down, he began to unravel one of his socks.

Digger's idea was taking shape. He lit his electric torch, and put it in the plastic bag, which he then filled with gas, using his kettle to pipe it into the bag. When the bag swelled up huge, he tied the neck with the sock wool.

The moon would not be up for two hours yet — but Digger Marr's shining plastic moon took its place. The whole bag glowed with light as Digger floated it high above his head. He made for the Indian village, and as he drew near, he pulled the glowing bag down slowly a foot at a time. Would his strange plan work?

It did! The superstitious Indians saw the gleaming sphere coming down towards them. They gazed in awe at first — and then in terror. "See! The Moon is falling out of the sky!" croaked Fork Tongue the medicine man. And every man, woman and child streamed out of the village, all quaking with fright.

There were four bears, and those first shots at long range did no more than sting them to fury. Digger looked round wildly. There was no refuge for him anywhere in the bare and wind-swept snow. But wait — the wardrobe! Digger wrenched open a door and dived inside, then wriggled round among the furs to open the door a crack and fire at the leading bear. A ferocious roar told Digger that he had winged the brute.

But he couldn't hope to stop them all. In the end they would surely smash the wardrobe to matchwood. At this desperate moment, it was the moon that saved Digger. Not his artificial moon, but the real one. It had risen some time ago, and restored the courage of the Piutes. They streamed back to their village, saw the trail of the vanished wardrobe, and found it the centre of this strange attack by the bear pack.

Crazy Horse and Crooked Nose led the charge upon the bears, and the arrows of the Piutes proved more deadly than Digger's bullets. The wounded bear was shot down, and the rest fled. Crazy Horse was jubilant. The Mirror Box was his again.

Inside the wardrobe, Digger shuddered. Had he fallen from the frying pan into the fire?

Then, with a flash of inspiration — he spoke! — in hollow, ghostly tones.

THE MIRROR BOX OF THE PALEFACE MUST GO BACK TO THE WOODEN WIGWAM, OR GREAT MISFORTUNE WILL BEFALL THE PIUTE TRIBE. THE SPIRIT OF THE MIRROR BOX HAS SPOKEN.

Digger heard the frightened gasps of the braves. He held his breath and remained stiff and still. A babble of voices broke out, then after a long pause he felt the wardrobe being lifted and carried away.

In a solemn procession led by the Chief, Digger's wandering wardrobe went home to stay.

WARDROBE, GOLD-DUST, FURS. I'VE SAVED THE LOT! AND SAVED MY OWN SKIN AS WELL.

From then on the Piutes were very friendly to the prospector, and he noticed that his Redskin visitors always gazed fearfully at the wardrobe and bowed to it. But never again did an Indian lay a hand on it.

"BEEN THERE, DONE IT!"

If **Jimmy Watson** hadn't been such a modest lad those words might have become his motto. The incredible power of the magic patch on the seat of his pants could take young Jimmy anywhere, at any time to rub shoulders with anyone! Is it any wonder **Jimmy's Magic Patch** became one of the most popular stories in **Beano's** history.

After reading this selection of tales from the comic's weekly issues, we're sure you'll agree that 1950 was a vintage year for time travel.

SORRY—
NO
BANANAS
TO-DAY

JIMMY and his MAGIC PATCH

1 — Jimmy Watson had a face as long as a big fiddle. He was just going outside to have a kick at his brand-new football when his Ma called, "You come back here, Jimmy Watson. It's time you did some work in the house." Poor Jimmy was sent to polish the little round mahogany table in the best room. "And no football for you till I can see my face in that table," snapped Mrs Watson. Jimmy squatted down on the floor and set to work.

2 — Only that morning at school, teacher had been telling Jimmy's class about King Arthur and the Knights of the Round Table. "I wouldn't mind polishing King Arthur's Round Table — that's something worth doing," muttered Jimmy. Suddenly everything went black and Jimmy hastily shut his eyes. He had a feeling that he was flying through space. When he opened his eyes he was still under a table — but it wasn't his mother's.

3 — The truth dawned on Jimmy. He was actually underneath King Arthur's Round Table and he could hear the hum of voices above him. You can guess what had happened. In the seat of Jimmy's pants was a Magic Patch which could whisk Jimmy back through time. Jimmy had wanted a chance of polishing King Arthur's Round Table and the Patch had granted the wish, whisking the lad back through the centuries. Jimmy couldn't help

giving a loud whistle of astonishment and the next minute he was hauled out from under the table. Seated round were the stately Knights of the Round Table. King Arthur gave Jimmy a shake. "What are you doing here, boy?" he boomed. "Speak up! I won't eat you!" Jimmy swallowed hard, knowing it would be useless to explain. But he had to think of some excuse. "Er — came to see if I could be a Knight," he blurted out.

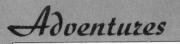

4 — A roar of laughter went up at Jimmy's words. King Arthur held up his hand for silence. He had taken a liking to Jimmy. "Very well, my boy!" he said, a twinkle in his eye. "A Knight you shall be — but first you must prove worthy of the honour." The good King gave orders to his followers and soon Jimmy was fitted with a coat of mail, some armour, a shield and a sword as big as himself.

5 — They gave him a steed, too. It was a gentle old mule, but Jimmy didn't mind. Tucking his tin of polish in his belt he mounted his "charger". "I'll do something to earn my knighthood," he called as he rode off. Jimmy's chance came sooner than he expected. He hadn't gone far over the hills when some riders came into view. One was a young girl and when she saw Jimmy she waved frantically. "Help!" she cried. "Help!"

6 — Some distance behind the riders lay a stranded coach. Then Jimmy realised at a glance that the coach had been held up by a gang of robbers and the girl kidnapped. "The rotters!" he muttered. "I'll give 'em a pasting." But how? He saw the girl and her captor race off along a road which wound round the foot of the rugged hills in a wide arc. "The first thing to do is to get ahead of them," muttered Jimmy. "I'll take a short cut."

7 — Up the hill charged Jimmy. From the top he saw the two riders following the road which led towards a little wooden bridge across a stream. Then Jimmy had one of his bright ideas, but he had to reach that bridge quickly — long before the riders did. He looked carefully at the long, smooth slope, and then unslung his shield. In a moment Jimmy was whizzing downhill, using the shield like a sledge.

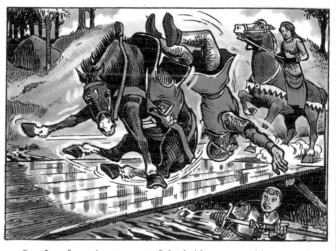

8 — The mule had taken a fancy to Jimmy and it followed slowly behind, but before it could say "Hee-haw," Jimmy was at the foot of the slope and racing for the bridge. Swiftly Jimmy got out his tin of polish, shook up the liquid and began to polish furiously at the surface of the bridge. Mrs Watson would have been amazed to see how fast her son really could polish!

9 — In a few minutes part of the bridge was as shiny as a piece of glass. Then Jimmy heard the riders approaching and nipped under the bridge to watch. The kidnapper was leading the way, and he rode straight on to the bridge. Then — whoosh! — the horse skidded on the shiny surface, lost its footing, and pitched its rider out of the saddle.

10 — The ruffian crashed full-length on the planks. In an instant, Jimmy was out from underneath the bridge, his sword at the kidnapper's throat. The man was too dazed to offer resistance. Jimmy found that the girl was a niece of King Arthur, and soon Jimmy, the girl, and the captured robber, were back at King Arthur's court. There the grateful King presented Jimmy with a pair of golden spurs. He had earned his spurs — he was a fully-fledged knight!

11 — Jimmy had just fixed his spurs over his football boots when the Magic Patch whizzed him back to his Ma's front parlour. And Jimmy was as proud as a peacock as he strutted around the room with his spurs — until Ma came in. "Jimmy Watson!" she shrieked. "Where did you get those spurs? And look at the mess they're making of my floor!" Jimmy didn't try to explain. He fled. But the funny thing now is that Ma Watson never has to ask Jimmy twice to polish that little round table!

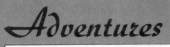

1 — In Jimmy Watson's school the gymnastics class was in full swing. Jimmy and his pals were practising "pyramids" and, as Jimmy was a sturdy lad, he was given a position to hold bang in the middle of the pyramid. Our pal wasn't happy about that. His legs ached under the strain, and his arms were nearly pulled out of their sockets. Worst of all, the shaky feet of Billy Dodds were grinding into Jimmy's shoulders. "Mind my ears, you chump!" hissed Jimmy, wriggling uncomfortably.

2 — "Keep still, Watson!" ordered Mr Sprogg the gym teacher. "You'll bring the pyramid down!" Jimmy gritted his teeth. "I wish I'd more practice at building pyramids," he panted. All of a sudden our Jimmy was no longer a part of that pyramid. He had made a wish and the Magic Patch on the seat of his pants was going to grant it. It whisked Jimmy out of the pyramid and away through space. The pyramid collapsed, and the howls those boys made could have been heard in Egypt.

3 — And that's exactly where our Jimmy was going — off to Egypt! Not modern Egypt. Oh, no! — Egypt of nearly six thousand years ago, at a time when the ancient Egyptians were building the Pyramids. What's more, Jimmy landed right beside a huge block of stone which was being dragged on a cart towards a half-finished Pyramid. Pulling the cart were a hundred sweating slaves.

4 — Immediately Jimmy was spotted by a big, tough Egyptian overseer who thought our pal was a slave trying to escape. Crack-crack! The leather thongs of a whip whistled round Jimmy's ears. "Dog of a slave!" bellowed the overseer. "Get back on the drag-rope of the cart!" Crack! The great whip curled around Jimmy's shoulders, driving him to task.

5 — Soon Jimmy was toiling with the other slaves who were helping to build the giant Pyramid. "That pesky Magic Patch!" muttered Jimmy, as the slave-driver's whip kept him sweating on the rope. The Patch had played a trick on Jimmy. It had granted his wish to practise building pyramids — but not the kind Jimmy meant! At last the sun began to set and work ceased on the Pyramid. The slaves were then herded into a huge open enclosure where they were shut up for the night.

6 — When the gate clanged shut Jimmy looked around him. Most of the slaves were dropping with fatigue. Day in, day out, they had laboured under their cruel task masters to build the Pyramid. Jimmy felt sorry for the poor fellows. He examined the walls of the pen. They were sheer and nearly twenty feet high. Suddenly a gleam came into Jimmy's eye. He hauled a notebook from his pocket and turned over the pages. It was his school P.T. notebook giving directions on how to build human pyramids.

7 — "What is that you have there, boy?" asked a voice. Jimmy looked round. Two of the slaves were peering over his shoulder. Jimmy grinned. "This little book is going to help us escape," he chuckled. "Listen." Carefully Jimmy explained his plan to the two men. Their eyes glowed with hope. Never in their wildest dreams had they ever expected to escape from the cruel Egyptians. Quickly the two men passed on Jimmy's plan to the other slaves, and with Jimmy in command, the whole bunch set to work to build a huge pyramid against the enclosure wall. Not a sound betrayed their movements.

8 — Slave after slave joined the pyramid till at last the pyramid was high enough for a man to reach the top of the wall. The rest was easy. The other men climbed the pyramid and dropped to freedom outside the wall. Jimmy saw to it that those who formed the pyramid were helped over the wall by means of a rope fashioned from men's clothing. In half an hour the enclosure was empty and the slaves were racing to safety.

9 — Jimmy was among the last to leave and carefully he picked his way between the tents of the Egyptian soldiers asleep outside the great pen. Then suddenly the worst happened. He tripped over a water jug lying on the ground and boo-oom! — the deafening peal of a gong split the silence of the night. Jimmy's head had banged against the huge gong used to rouse the slaves for their day's toil on the Pyramid.

10 — Jimmy's heart sank. "Golly! That's torn it!" he gasped. Already the Egyptian guards were leaping from their tents. "The slaves are escaping!" went up the cry. Jimmy took to his heels with a dozen guards racing after him. Then suddenly the Magic Patch came to the rescue. With startling suddenness Jimmy was whisked away into the air before the very eyes of the astonished Egyptians. The Patch whizzed Jimmy back to modern times again, right into the school gymnasium.

11 — Jimmy gaped about him in astonishment. His schoolmates were busy bandaging bruises and cuts on their bodies — the result of the pyramid collapsing. "Crumbs! What's happened here?" gasped Jimmy. He soon found out. "There's Watson!" roared Billy Dodds. "Grab him, boys! We'll teach him to make a mess of our pyramid." Jimmy Watson fled. Next day his chums had cooled down a bit, but nowadays whenever anyone mentions pyramids, Jimmy is nowhere to be seen. He's had enough of them!

1 — Jimmy Watson was late for school. As he sprinted down the main street of his home town, the clock on the Old Steeple boomed nine o'clock and Jimmy put an extra spurt on. No wonder his pals called him Jet-propelled Jimmy! But there was a special reason for Jim being late. The school janitor was sick and Jimmy had been told to collect the school keys from the janitor's house on his way to school. The school couldn't be opened till Jimmy got there! As Jimmy skidded into School Lane a picture of the liner Queen Mary caught his eye.

2 — Jimmy loved ships, especially the two famous "Queens". "Gosh!" thought Jimmy as he flashed past the travel agency window. "She's from Scotland — I didn't know that. I've seen the Elizabeth, but I'd like to see the Queen Mary some time." The next moment Jimmy was no longer in School Lane. He was being whirled through space at an alarming rate. The Magic Patch on Jimmy's pants was going to grant his wish, but in a strange way. In two shakes Jimmy was whisked back to the year 1568 and dropped gently in a castle in Loch Leven, in Scotland.

3 — Jimmy stood gaping round the courtyard in amazement. He knew the Patch had been at work, but why had it dumped him inside an ancient castle? Jimmy's thoughts were rudely interrupted by a voice bellowing in his ear. "Ah, you must be the new kitchen boy," boomed a burly man in cook's dress. "Well, don't stand there staring! Into the kitchen with you."

4 — In the kitchen an ox was being roasted over a fire. "You're just in time to help with dinner for the castle guard and the Queen!" boomed the cook. "Ye didn't know Queen Mary was prisoner here, did ye? Now get busy turning the roast!" The Patch had taken Jimmy to see a Queen Mary from Scotland all right — only it was Mary, Queen of Scots!

5 — Queen Mary's faithful page was working in the kitchen. Jimmy took a liking to the boy and he knew why he was looking so glum. "Cheer up," whispered Jimmy to the lad. "It's a rotten shame that the Queen should be shut up in this castle. We'll help her to escape." The cook gave a loud bellow. "Stop talking, you two! Here, take these trays of refreshments to the Queen!" Soon Jimmy and his chum were on their way to the Queen's prison in the tower. At the tower entrance stood a sentry, and as the boys approached he held out a bunch of keys.

6 — In a whisper the page explained to Jimmy that every time he visited the tower he was given the bunch of keys. There were two doors to unlock on the way up to the Queen's prison. As soon as the page left the tower he had to lock all the doors again and hand back the keys to the sentry. The sight of the keys set Jimmy thinking and by the time he had reached the Queen's room, our pal had a plan. Jimmy bowed low as the page lifted the school cap from his head and ushered him into the presence of the Queen. Jimmy was thrilled to meet such a famous lady.

7 — Soon Jimmy Watson and the Queen were best of friends. "Your Majesty," said Jimmy quickly. "I have a plan to help you to escape from the castle." Pulling the school keys from his pocket Jimmy began to talk like a gramophone in a hurry. The lad had noticed that the school keys and the tower keys looked very much alike. "All we have to do is swop 'em round, you see?" he added. "Leave it to Jimmy Watson."

8 — The boys left the Queen and made their way back to the courtyard, taking care to lock all the doors with the tower keys. Then when it came to returning the bunch of keys to the sentry, it was Jimmy who handed them over — only it was the bunch of school keys he gave to the sentry. The man was too lazy to inspect the keys, and the page took good care to keep the tower keys hidden. Then the boys set to work laying their final plans.

9 — The page had noticed that about midnight the tower sentry had a habit of dozing off. So, just after twelve o'clock, the two boys crept across the courtyard. Sure enough, the sentry was snoring like a pig. Jimmy grinned as he saw the school keys fixed to the man's belt, then, with the tower keys, he set to work to free the Queen. Five minutes later the two boys were escorting Queen Mary across the dark courtyard.

10 — One of the keys fitted a small door in the wall near the tower and Jimmy lost no time in unlocking that door. The waters of Loch Leven lapped against the steps below the door and in the dim light Jimmy and his friends could see the dark shape of a boat moored to the wall. As the Queen appeared, an old boatman rose from the boat and helped the Queen aboard. Jimmy and the page had arranged things well.

11 — In a few moments the row-boat was gliding across the loch. The Queen and her page were full of gratitude to Jimmy Watson. "We have no further use for these keys, Your Majesty," said the page. And Jimmy's heart skipped a beat. He had suddenly remembered that he had left the school keys behind in the castle. Jimmy made a snatch at the tower keys as the page tossed them into the loch, and just then the Magic Patch began to whisk Jimmy back home again.

12 — Next moment Jimmy found himself back in School Lane. "Watson! Watson!" called a voice. "Hurry up with the school keys! It's after nine!" It was Mr Twitt, the headmaster, speaking. With quaking knees Jimmy trotted to the door of the school. Perhaps one of the tower keys might fit the school door. But Jimmy tried without success. "I — I must have brought the wrong keys, sir," gasped Jimmy, while his pals gave a cheer. Thanks to the Magic Patch there was no school that morning!

Adventures

1 — Jimmy Watson was as happy as a dog with two tails — he had just become the owner of a smashing new model railway, complete with streamlined engine and trucks. It was a gift from his Uncle John in Scotland, and it had only arrived that morning. Jimmy lovingly stroked the sleek body of the engine. "It's a real beauty!" he said to his Pa. "Gosh! Engines have certainly changed since Stephenson's Rocket." Jimmy gave a chuckle, and added, "I wish I knew what George Stephenson would have said if he had seen my new engine!"

2 — The next moment Jimmy was no longer in the Watsons' front parlour. Still gripping his new model train, he was whizzing back through time at an alarming rate. The cause of this was the Magic Patch on the seat of Jimmy's trousers. This amazing Patch had the power to whisk Jimmy back to any period in history — and now, in two shakes, he was back in the year 1829. With a gentle bump he landed outside a small workshop in Newcastle. The name on the wall was "Geo. Stephenson," and there was the famous inventor himself at the doorway!

3 — Jimmy gave George Stephenson time to recover from the shock of seeing a boy suddenly appear out of the blue. Then he introduced himself. "I see you need an apprentice," added the bold lad. "I'd like the job, please." Stephenson nodded in a dazed kind of way, and ushered Jimmy into the workshop. Then the inventor saw Jimmy's model engine. "What on earth's that contraption?" he asked. Jimmy told him. "A model of a railway engine?" echoed Stephenson, and he burst out laughing.

4 — Stephenson looked strangely at Jimmy. "The poor boy must be queer in the head," he thought, then added aloud. "That's nothing like a real railway engine. Come and I will show you what I mean, for I am building a railway engine now!" Jimmy was taken into another part of the workshop, and there he saw the famous Rocket. "My boy," said Stephenson gravely, "in a few days my engine will be completed, and it will travel at the breakneck speed of ten miles per hour!"

5 — While Jimmy and his new friend were talking excitedly about the Rocket, trouble was brewing in the livery stables across the street. A group of coachmen were muttering amongst themselves, and pointing threateningly at the workshop. Unknown to Stephenson the coachmen were plotting against him, for they were afraid his new invention would take away their trade.

6 — In the gathering darkness, the plotters, armed with heavy hammers, left their stables and crept towards the workshop. They peered through the lighted window, then one of them gave a signal. The next moment the men burst inside, and, before Jimmy and Stephenson could bat an eyelid, they were roughly seized and hurled to the ground.

7 — Then Stephenson was quickly bound to a chair and Jimmy was gruffly ordered to sit on the floor beside him. "And not a cheep out o' either o' you," snarled one coachman, "or you'll feel the weight o' my fist." Jimmy was puzzled, but it was clear that Stephenson knew very well what the coachmen meant to do. As the men moved over to the Rocket, Stephenson bent close to Jimmy. "They're going to wreck the Rocket!" he whispered fiercely. Jimmy decided he'd have to do something about this.

8 — Then the bold James caught sight of Stephenson's pet cat. It was crawling through a small opening in the foot of the door. A sudden plan came to the boy. With one eye on the coachmen, he quickly wrote something in two pages of his notebook, and cautiously tore out the sheets. Within reach lay his toy train, with the engine's motor fully wound. Quickly Jimmy fixed the two sheets of paper to the train. Then he started the motor. The train sped forwards towards the opening in the door.

9 — The coachmen were stripping off their heavy coats making ready to batter the Rocket into scrap metal. They were talking hoarsely to themselves, and their voices drowned the slight noise made by the train as it passed unnoticed through the opening in the door and out into the street. The train fairly raced over the cobbles and it had gone nearly a hundred yards when two old-time policemen suddenly spotted it.

10 — "'Ere, Bert!" gasped one of the bobbies. "W-what is that odd —" He broke off with a start. He had seen the message fixed to the side of the train. "I know Mr Stephenson!" snapped the bobby. "He's an inventor. This must be one of his inventions. He's in trouble. Come on!" Just as the coachmen were ready to start their work of destruction the door of the workshop suddenly burst open and in raced half a dozen bobbies.

11 — Jimmy gave a whoop of joy. The bobbies had arrived in the nick of time. They took in the situation at a glance, and snatched the hammers from the hands of the wreckers. Stephenson explained matters to the policemen, and the coachmen were soon marched off to jail. The famous inventor couldn't thank Jimmy enough. "My boy!" he said. "But for you and your — er — gadget, my engine would have been ruined beyond repair. How can I ever reward you?" "Just give me a ride on the Rocket!" said Jimmy. And Stephenson was only too pleased to oblige. So, when the Rocket had its first trial trip, Jimmy Watson was on the tender. But he hadn't been there two minutes when the Magic Patch whisked him and his toy train home again.

The editors of **Dandy** and **Beano** can always be relied upon to produce extra-special Christmas issues, with the comics' superstars like Desperate Dan and Lord Snooty hosting the Yuletide celebrations. And there were times when the adventure story heroes joined in the festive fun. This heartwarming **Danny Longlegs** tale appeared in the 1946 Christmas **Dandy**.

DANNY LONGLEGS

"CLEAR out, you vagabonds!" Miser Crane's angry voice didn't sound nice at all to Danny Longlegs. The ten-foot schoolboy of Sleepy Valley had climbed Primrose Hill to find a Christmas tree. With him were Bunty Evans and his pup Bobo. Danny desperately needed a tree for it was Christmas Eve. And his little cousin Harry, staying with Danny for the holidays, had hurt his leg while skating and had to stay in bed. There would be no party for Harry unless Longlegs could find a tree.

2 — Danny had only stopped to peep in at the cheery scene in Miser Crane's big parlour. There was a bright fire, and a big plumduff, and a tree with candles and decorations. But the rich old skinflint hated anyone to see his treasures. He was too mean to realise that his tiny grandchild, Hilda, would have enjoyed herself more amongst youngsters than alone with her grumpy old Grandad. Danny moved off. Not far from the house were two woodcutters, and they were in a proper pickle.

3 — They were cutting down trees with a double-handled saw. One chap was standing on a tree stump, and he was all right. But the other couldn't reach his saw handle because he kept sinking into the snow. "Here, big fellow, lend a hand, will you?" asked one of the foresters. "Gladly," answered Longlegs. "Maybe you could let me have a little Christmas tree for our party, eh?" He had seized the handle and begun sawing, and the blade was biting deeply into the tree-trunk.

4 — Puffing, the woodcutter smiled cheerily. "Take any one you want, boy," he said, "and you can borrow my sledge to take it home, too." With Danny's help the tree-felling job was soon finished, and the grateful foresters selected a nice tree for the boys. It was placed on the sledge, and the pals set off down the hill, waving goodbye to the woodcutters. But there was trouble ahead for the sledgers. Miser Crane had watched through his window and seen all that happened. "Ho! A thief!" he cried.

5 — While Longlegs helped his workmen he didn't interfere, but his greediness got the better of him when he saw Danny taking one of his fir-trees. Snatching his whip, he raced pell-mell to his stable and harnessed his horse to a sleigh. Off he drove at a mad speed down the winding path. Longlegs and Bunty were taking the short way down, which was a mistake. Right in front of them was a sudden drop into a deep chasm.

6 — Miser crane saw them whizzing past out of his reach, and was so excited that he shook up his reins and urged the horse on to the hillside to cut off the boys' escape. Crash! A tree stump hidden in the snow caught the front of old Crane's sleigh. The harness broke, the horse fell, the sleigh rose up on its front end, and Miser Crane shot out of his seat and skidded on his back down the snowy slope — right over the edge of the cliff!

7 — Sticking out one long leg, Danny was able to stop his sled from hurtling over the edge. He swerved madly, using his foot as a brake in the snow. Horrified, he saw the old miser shoot off into space, and couldn't do a thing to save him. The big boy hurriedly drew the sledge back from the brink of the cliff and ran to peep over, expecting to see Miser Crane lying in a crumpled heap at the bottom, for it was a long drop, even though the snow lay thick on the floor of the valley below.

8 — But Miser Crane had been lucky. Shooting over the edge, he had turned upside-down and by sheer chance his short winter coat had caught on a branch of a tall tree. He was still in great danger, for the thin branch was cracking under his weight. "Help me!" cried the helpless man. "I'm falling!" There wasn't a moment to spare if Miser Crane was to be saved, so Longlegs got moving. Swiftly he swung himself over the cliff edge. He had only one chance to save the miser's life.

9 — Hanging by his hands, the big boy groped for a toe-hold in the rocks, rested one foot in it, and then stretched his other long leg out towards the frightened Mr Crane. Just in time! Danny just managed to yell — "Hang on to my leg, Mr Crane!" — and then the branch which supported the old man gave way. It was a stiff job for Longlegs to climb up with the miser's weight dragging on his leg, but he succeeded at last.

10 — What a change came over the greedy rich man then! He sat in the snow for a while, saying never a word. Then he rose, offered his hand to Danny, and humbly thanked him. "Not for saving my worthless life," he said, "but for those few minutes when I hung between life and death. For the first time I saw myself as other people see me — a mean, rude, nasty old man! But I'll never be like that again! From now on I'll change!"

11 — He kept his word. From then on Mr Crane became a kind, generous and cheerful man who spent all his time and money making people happy. Longlegs and his pals were the first to benefit by the miser's change of heart. The old man insisted that Danny and all his friends, his parents, his schoolteacher — even Cousin Harry on his bed, and his pup Bobo — should spend Christmas at the big house. What a party that was! Mr Crane spared no expense. There was enough food to feed a regiment, gifts for everyone, and the jolliest fun and games you ever heard of. Little Hilda hardly knew her snappy old Grandad, he had become so jolly and kind. And she enjoyed that Christmas better than any other she had known. Danny Longlegs had done everybody in Sleepy Valley a good turn when he saved Miser Crane's life. The house on Primrose Hill became a happy place for Hilda.

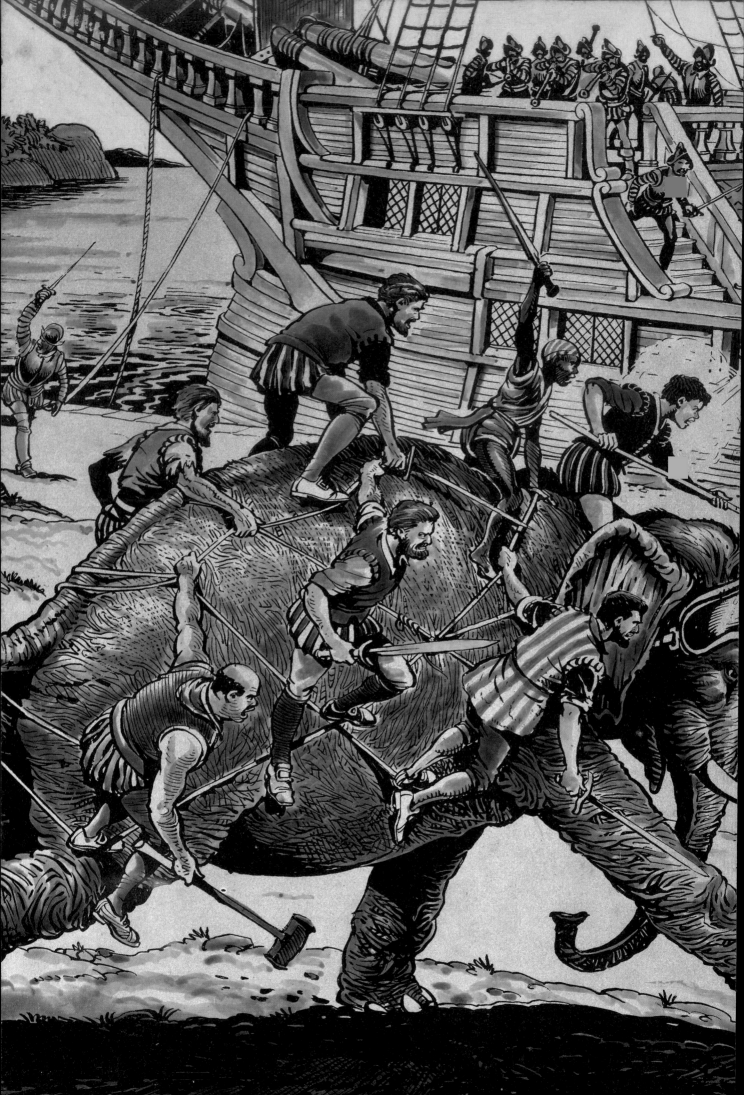